D1408243

INTRODUCTION

On 26 October 1977, in Somalia, Ali Maow Maalim, an unvaccinated hospital employee, developed a typical smallpox rash. It was two weeks after he had been in close contact with two smallpox cases whom he had accompanied to the hospital isolation camp. This was the world's last case of smallpox and Ali Maow Maalin is a living monument to an unprecedented international effort to combat and eradicate a dreaded disease from the face of the earth.

Only 10 years before in 1967, 31 countries with over one billion people experienced 10–15 million smallpox cases and more than two million deaths. No country was safe from the importation of smallpox, and the world continued to live with this scourge until the World Health Organization (WHO) intensified its worldwide efforts to eradicate smallpox.

This story recounts the devastation of a terrible disease on human civilization. It is also a story of mankind's triumph over smallpox and that of the brave men and women who made bold decisions against all odds.

Even though the smallpox vaccine had been available for more than 170 years, it was only after the World Health Organization's decision to eradicate smallpox in 1966, did the world begin to rid itself of this ancient scourge. A brave group then set forth to find and eradicate all of the world's smallpox cases. This is the story of their success.

NOTE TO READERS

"Since smallpox is the first major human disease to have been eradicated, and since the battle against it was waged in remote areas far from the gaze of television cameras, the younger generations may have difficulty in appreciating the nature and magnitude of the task of global eradication. Yet, when the history of the twentieth century is written from the standpoint of the twenty-first, the eradication of smallpox will undoubtedly be ranked with the mastery of flight, the harnessing of nuclear energy, and the first steps in the exploration of space." — *Quote from Dr. Halfdan Mahler, WHO Director-General, September 1987*

A Congratulatory Message from Sanofi Pasteur on the 30th Anniversary
of Smallpox Eradication

Sanofi pasteur has a long legacy of disease prevention, which began with Louis Pasteur's success against rabies and was exemplified in Charles Mérieux's efforts to make vaccines available to millions. However, one story epitomizes the company founders' shared passion for promoting and protecting public health: the quest to eradicate smallpox.

Charged with improving the vaccine to quell the smallpox epidemic in the United States, a young American scientist named Richard Slee traveled to France in 1893. He returned home with a French smallpox vaccine formula from Institut Pasteur and opened the laboratories that today serve as sanofi pasteur's largest U.S. site.

In Toronto, Connaught Laboratories — now the Connaught Campus of sanofi pasteur Limited — began producing smallpox vaccine in 1917. By the mid-1960s, the possibility of eradicating smallpox became increasingly apparent, in part through Connaught Laboratories' close working relationship with the World Health Organization's smallpox eradication program. The WHO designated the Canadian labs as the Regional Smallpox Vaccine Reference Center for the Western Hemisphere, responsible for promoting the use and application of testing standards. At the same time, the Institut Mérieux in France began mass producing a reliable supply of smallpox vaccine, a cornerstone of the global effort.

The contributions of all parent companies are forever memorialized in sanofi pasteur's vision of "a world in which no one suffers or dies from a vaccine-preventable disease." Thanks to the generations of dedicated scientists, vaccine advocates and proponents of global solidarity who followed in the pioneers' paths, mass immunization programs successfully eradicated smallpox in 1980, enabling us this year to celebrate 30 years without resurgence.

Through education, widespread immunization campaigns, continued funding of vaccine research and development, and the example of our success against smallpox, we not only seek to reduce the spread of serious infectious diseases, we begin to envision a day they will disappear entirely. In remembering the journey that brought us to this 30th anniversary of smallpox eradication and the lessons learned, we gain new hope that the elimination of diseases such as polio, malaria and tuberculosis are truly within our reach.

May 1, 2010

SMALLPOX ZERO

AN ILLUSTRATED HISTORY OF SMALLPOX AND ITS ERADICATION

COMMEMORATING THE 30TH ANNIVERSARY OF THE ERADICATION OF SMALLPOX
MAY 2010

*

ILLUSTRATED AND NARRATED BY
JONATHAN ROY

This Illustrated History of Smallpox is a project of former smallpox eradication workers from around the world who together formed the Smallpox Eradication Commemoration 2010 (SEC2010) Secretariat at the Emory Global Health Institute, Emory University, Atlanta, Georgia, USA. SEC2010 has supported three different activities — a monument placed at WHO headquarters in Geneva, an international symposium in Rio de Janeiro, and this historical novel that is provided to readers around the world. The novel has been supported by sanofi pasteur, the vaccines division of sanofi-aventis Group, and many former smallpox eradication workers worldwide. Reproduction of this document without specific written permission from the SEC2010 Secretariat is prohibited.

Photo courtesy of WHO

CREDITS

Illustrations, text selections, and layouts, Jonathan Roy, New York

Document production funded by Sanofi Pasteur

Published by: Nic Buchanan, Umlando Wezithombe, African Comic Production House, Johannesburg, South Africa

French translation by Elisabeth Paret and Mathilde Durif, Sanofi Pasteur
Russian translation by Lev Khodakevich, Moscow and editing by Yuri A. Avdeev, Chelyabinsk, Russia

Printing supported in part by Sanofi Pasteur and Vestergaard Frandsen, Lausanne, Switzerland

ISBN 978-0-620-43765-3 Smallpox Illustrated History

Printed in Singapore

May 2010

Acknowledgements

The illustrator Jonathan P. Roy wishes to thank Donald A. Henderson, MD, MPH, David Heymann, MD, DTM&H, Stephen Jones, MD, MPH, Judith L. Kanne, RN, BA, Jean Roy and smallpox veterans who graciously reviewed this work and who provided the basic ideas for the narrative during its many years of preparation. Ideas for graphics and text were inspired and adapted from numerous worldwide publications and articles listed in Appendix III. Images from the World Health Bulletin on pages 47, 51, 58, and the hostage note on page 56 are courtesy of the WHO. Any misinterpretations or misrepresentations of facts are solely those of the author/illustrator.

Note
The health terminology used in this story may be new to some readers. Simple explanations of terms are provided in the Glossary in Appendix II.

CHAPTER ONE

THE RISE . . .

. . . OF THE LOATHSOME SMALLPOX

It all started more than 10,000 years ago . . .

. . . when humans turned from hunting and foraging . . .

. . . to farming.

THE SUSPECTED ORIGINS OF THE SMALLPOX VIRUS.....

"Smallpox probably began as an infection of lower mammals such as squirrels or rodents. At some point it infected a human, where presumably it adapted through mutation, leaving us with a virus that infects humans and sometimes higher primates such as orangutans and chimpanzees, but no other mammals. Thus there is no reservoir of smallpox in nature." *

– Quote from D.A. Henderson, 2007
Former Chief, WHO Smallpox Eradication Unit

*Infectious diseases are caused by germs found in water, food, soil, other mammals, fish, or insects. These are considered reservoirs from which humans then catch the disease.

Growing communities and populations facilitated person-to-person transmission of infectious diseases.

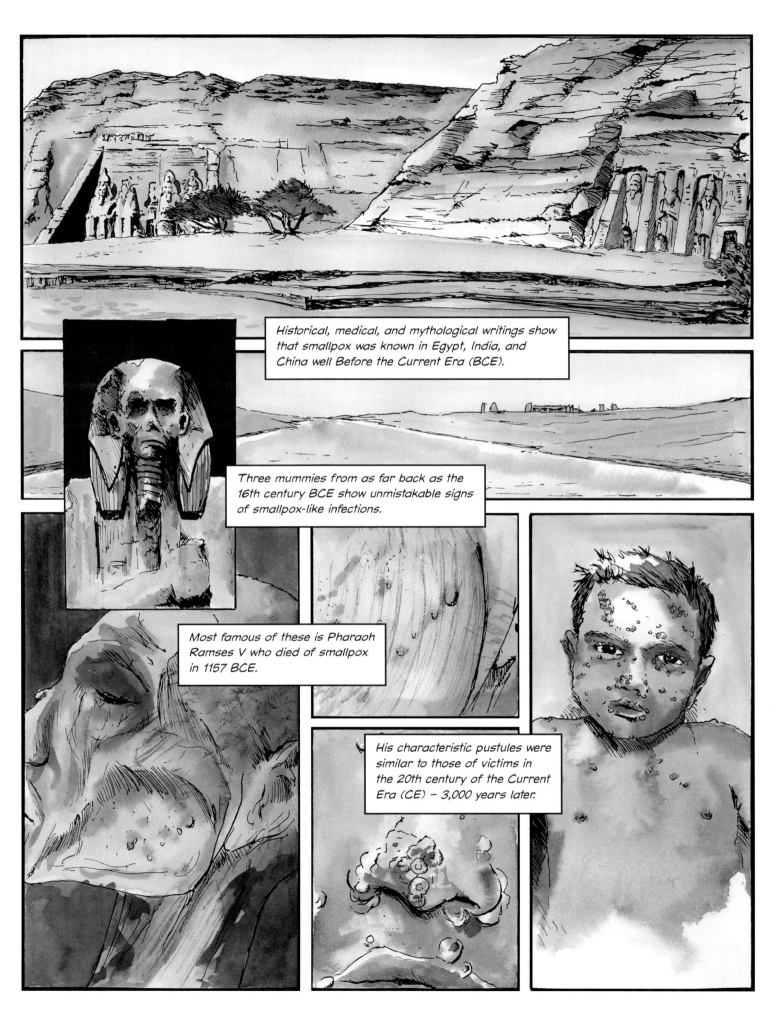

Historical, medical, and mythological writings show that smallpox was known in Egypt, India, and China well Before the Current Era (BCE).

Three mummies from as far back as the 16th century BCE show unmistakable signs of smallpox-like infections.

Most famous of these is Pharaoh Ramses V who died of smallpox in 1157 BCE.

His characteristic pustules were similar to those of victims in the 20th century of the Current Era (CE) – 3,000 years later.

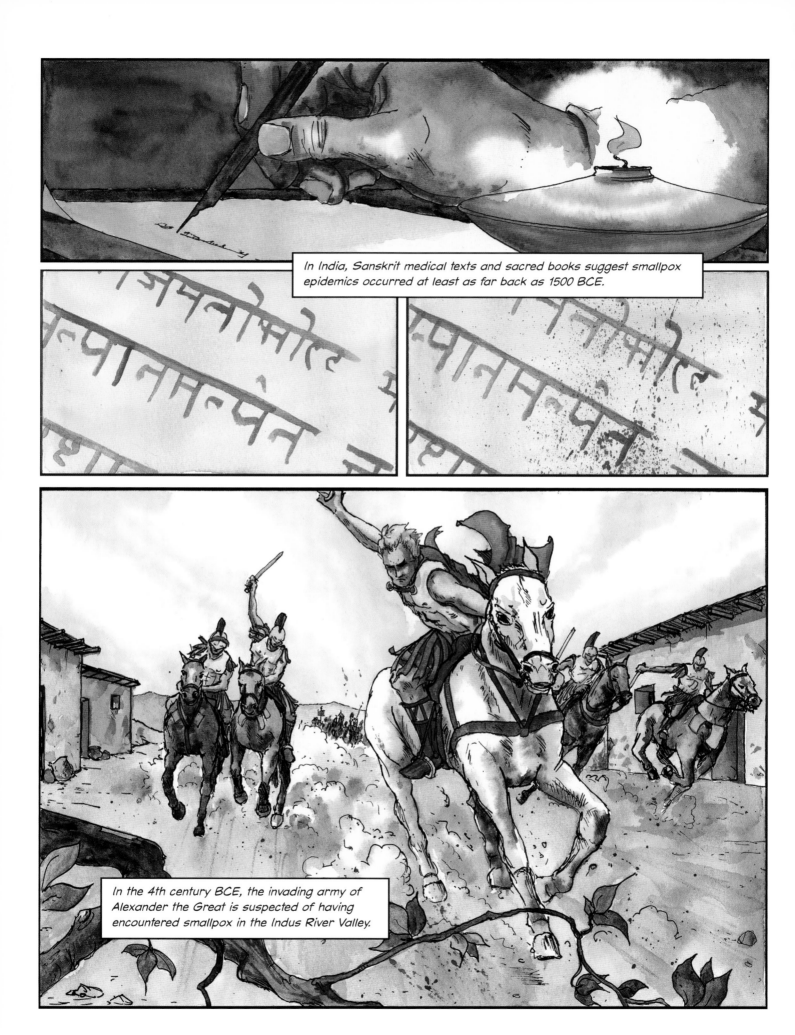

In India, Sanskrit medical texts and sacred books suggest smallpox epidemics occurred at least as far back as 1500 BCE.

In the 4th century BCE, the invading army of Alexander the Great is suspected of having encountered smallpox in the Indus River Valley.

Hittite invaders faced smallpox in Egypt.

In China, smallpox is alleged to have been imported by the Huns in 250 BCE.

The sickness was known as "Hunpox" by the Chinese.

In classical Greece, during the 5th century BCE, Thucydides described a plague which was possibly smallpox.

This smallpox plague in Greece was said to have come from Ethiopia and Egypt.

In the Middle East, the earliest smallpox cases may have originally come from trading caravans . . .

. . . and invading armies.

Smallpox was carried by army troops from Carthage and Rome . . .

. . . and spread.

As the centuries progressed, transmission continued.

Larger towns and cities sustained transmission in ever wider geographic areas.

From the religious pilgrimages so common in the Middle Ages . . .

. . . to knights and armies who sought to regain lands in the southern Mediterranean.

Traders and armies further spread smallpox throughout Europe, where increased population densities allowed the disease to establish itself.

By the 16th century CE, all of Europe knew of the deadly smallpox . . .

. . . and from European ports, explorers and sailors spread the disease to the New World.

And smallpox also spread with the slave trade.

The African slave trade resulted in repeated introductions of smallpox to the Caribbean, Mexico, and South America . . . the first being in 1507 when Hispaniola experienced disastrous epidemics that wiped out whole tribes.

Smallpox spread to Cuba in 1518 and to Puerto Rico in 1519 where over half the native population succumbed to the disease.

Populations in the Americas were hit particularly hard by the disease.

From the 16th through the 19th centuries, Native Americans were devastated by smallpox, killing 50 to 80% through the course of many epidemics.

Sometimes entire tribes disappeared as the small numbers of the epidemics' survivors were unable to feed themselves.

Epidemics swept from Mexico to Peru, ravaging the Aztecs, Mayas, and Incas – causing a higher proportion of deaths than in any other part of the world.

In North America in 1775, smallpox prolonged the siege of Boston by colonial forces at the outset of the American Revolution. General George Washington was wary of attacking Boston for fear his soldiers would catch smallpox.

Sumatra and Sarawak were ravaged in the 1780s.

In 1750, there were more than 40,000 deaths in Belém, Brazil.

A continent-wide epidemic hit South America in the years 1764–1765.

Similar devastation occurred in South Africa in the 1750s.

Great epidemics in India between 1868 and 1884 caused 25 million deaths in a total population of 180 million.

Once introduced to China and Korea, smallpox was a major endemic and epidemic disease through the centuries.

At one point only soldiers who had recovered from the disease were recruited to conquer new areas where smallpox was prevalent.

Smallpox was repeatedly imported into Japan from China and Korea from 585 CE onward. Records in Japan reveal periodic epidemics throughout the 18th century.

Temple records indicate a devastating epidemic in 1795 on the small island of Hachijo-Jima, where 1,200 cases occurred in a population of 1,400 – with 460 deaths.

13

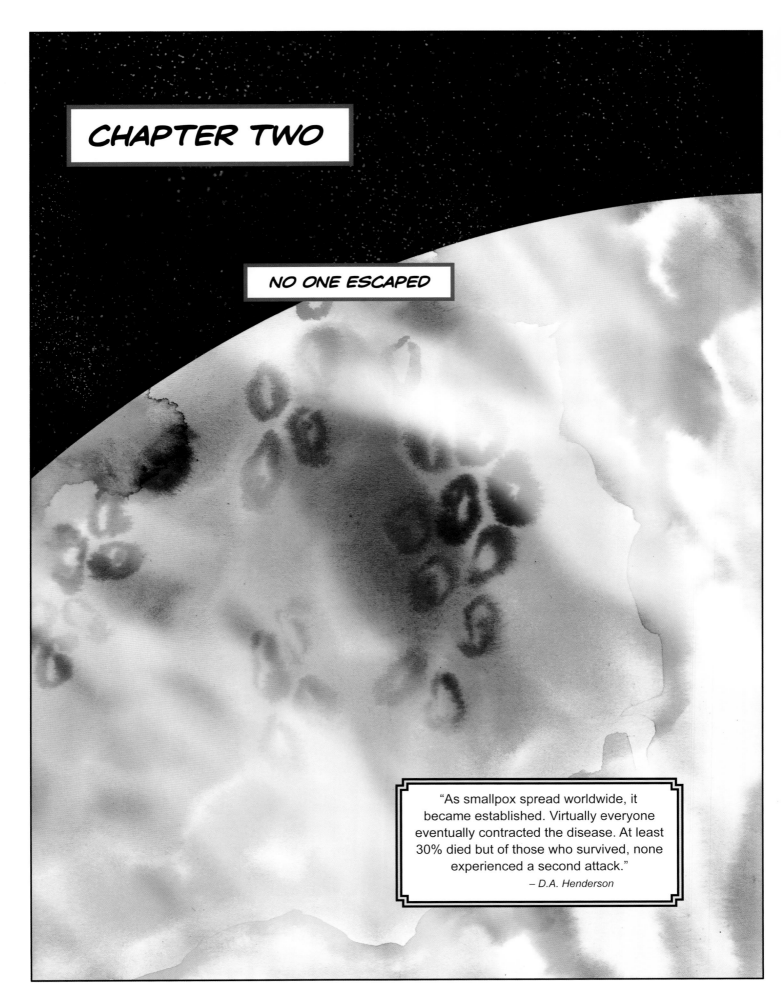

CHAPTER TWO

NO ONE ESCAPED

"As smallpox spread worldwide, it
became established. Virtually everyone
eventually contracted the disease. At least
30% died but of those who survived, none
experienced a second attack."
– D.A. Henderson

It was said that in parts of Central Europe, children were not given a name until they had survived smallpox.

Smallpox was history's most democratic scourge, striking royalty as well as peasants.

Smallpox ravaged the royals of England including Elizabeth I who luckily recovered.

Her successors in the House of Stuart were less fortunate. Princess Mary of England, her husband William II of Orange, and her brother the Duke of Gloucester all died of smallpox in their twenties and within a decade of each other.

From 1650–1700, Queen Mary II died of smallpox as well as her younger brother. A different Duke of Gloucester, son of Mary's sister Queen Anne, died at 11 years of age.

In Austria, 11 members of the reigning House of Hapsburg died of smallpox between 1654 and 1767.

In France, Louis XIV's heir, the Grand Dauphin, died of smallpox in 1711.

His great grandson and successor, Louis XV, died of smallpox after 59 years of reigning over France – on the eve of the French Revolution.

16

In the 18th century, five major epidemics occurred in London from 1719 to 1746, each killing thousands, mostly children.

In 1730 – 7% of New York City residents died of smallpox.

Similar epidemics struck cities across Europe.

Rome . . .

Berlin . . .

Geneva . . .

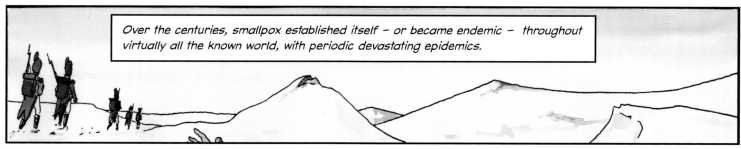

Over the centuries, smallpox established itself – or became endemic – throughout virtually all the known world, with periodic devastating epidemics.

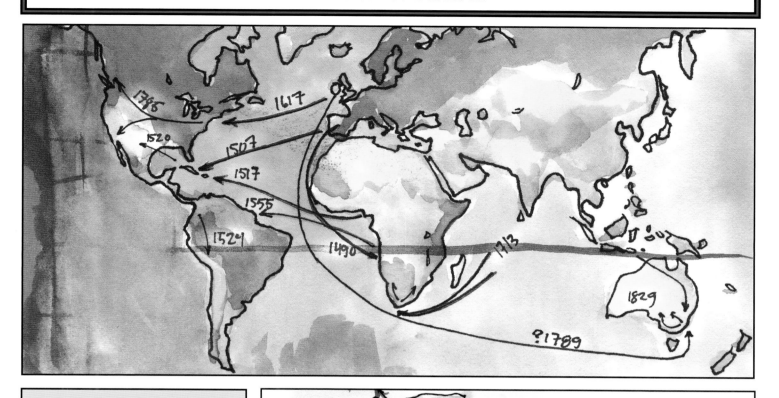

Smallpox was established in North Africa during the 8th century. It spread from there along the trade routes across the Sahara to the dense populations of western Africa during the 11th and 12th centuries.

On the eastern coast smallpox was imported periodically from India via Arab and Indian traders. The interior of the continent was probably smallpox-free until the 19th century.

Maps and text: Fenner F., D.A. Henderson, I. Arita, Z. Jesek, I.D. Ladnyi. *Smallpox and its Eradication.* Geneva: World Health Organization, 1988 and Hopkins, Donald R. *Princes and Peasants: Smallpox in History,* Chicago: University of Chicago Press, 1983

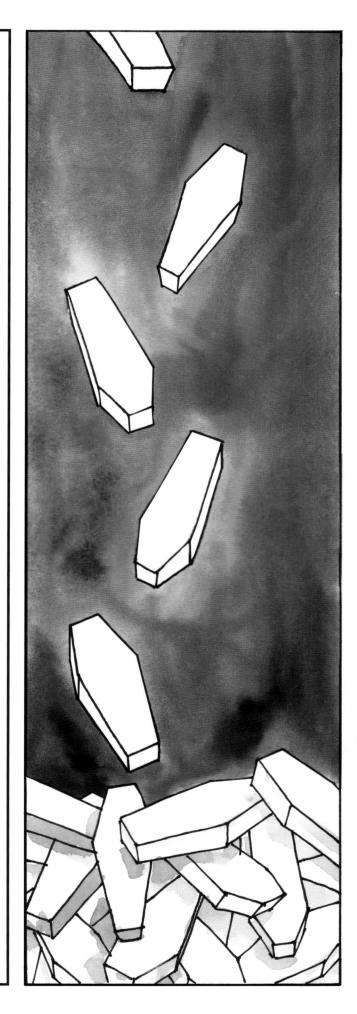

SOME FAMOUS PERSONS WHO DIED OF SMALLPOX

180 CE	Marcus Aurelius
754	Caliph Abbul al-Abbass al-Saffah
1368	King Thadominbya of Burma
1520	Aztec emperor Ciutlahuac (epidemic killed 3 million in Aztec, Mexico)
1534	King Boramaraja IV of Siam
1582	The King and Queen of Ceylon and all of their sons
1646	Prince Baltasar Carlos, heir to the Spanish throne
1650	William of Orange and his wife, Henrietta in England
1654	Emperor Ferdinand IV of Austria
1654	Emperor Gokomyo of Japan
1661	Emperor Fu-lin of China
1694	Queen Mary II of England at the age of 32
1700	King Nagassi of Ethiopia
1709	Emperor Higashiyama of Japan
1710	Emperor Joseph I of Austria
1711	Louis XIV's heir in France
1724	King Louis I of Spain
1730	Tsar Peter II of Russia
1736	Benjamin Franklin's son
1741	Ulrika Eleanora, Queen of Sweden
1774	King Louis XV of France at age 64

Adapted from "Smallpox: the triumph over the most terrible of the ministers of death," by N. Barquet and P. Domoningo, 1997.

CHAPTER THREE

DEITIES, DOCTORS, AND DIVINE
INTERVENTIONS

Throughout the ages smallpox was often associated with deities . . .

In the Hindu religion, Sitala Mata is considered to be the wife of the great god Shiva the Destroyer.

She is considered vengeful and wrathful, and has temples dedicated to her across India.

Shapona is the god of smallpox in the Yoruba culture in West Africa.

Shapona also became the object of worship in the New World – especially in Brazil and the Caribbean, as a result of the slave trade – where the god was known as Omolu.

Several centuries BCE, the Chinese smallpox goddess T'ou-Shen Niang-Niang was revered by Buddhists, Taoists, and Confucians alike.

Ma-Chen is the Chinese god that heals the ugly pustules of smallpox.

22

Chinzei Hachiro Tametomo (1139–1170), a skillful archer, was exiled to the island of Oshima. He is reputed to have prevented a smallpox demon from landing there. His image was hung on the walls to protect against smallpox.

In the 2nd century CE, Galen, a prominent Roman physician, described smallpox.

Hippocrates was among the first to describe what may have been outbreaks of smallpox disease.

Rhazes, a Persian-born physician (10th century CE), described and distinguished smallpox from other rash diseases.

The 5th century Bishop of Rheims (France), who was cannonized as St. Nicaise, was adopted as the patron saint of smallpox cases.

The causes of smallpox were thought to range from divine intervention (punishment for sins) . . .

. . . to imbalances among the four humors . . .

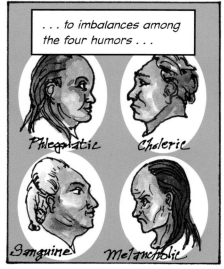

Phlegmatic
Choleric
Sanguine
Melancholic

. . . to changes in ambient temperatures . . .

. . . and to poisons invading the body.

In the 19th century, when vaccination was introduced, some religious leaders argued against intervening with God's will.

Future global eradication efforts of the 1960–70s were sometimes hampered by accusations of tampering with divine intent, especially in West Africa and India.

THE RED TREATMENT

Red paper and red cloth were hung around the beds of children with smallpox in China, India, Turkey, Asian Georgia, and Europe; even in western Africa, the Yoruba god of smallpox, Shapona, was associated with the color red.

In European countries the red treatment was practiced from the 12th century onward. When he caught smallpox, King Charles V of France (reigned 1364–1380) was dressed in a red shirt, red stockings, and red veil. Queen Elizabeth I of England was likewise wrapped in a red blanket when she fell ill with smallpox in 1562, and similar treatments were applied to other European monarchs.

This has no basis in science or fact.

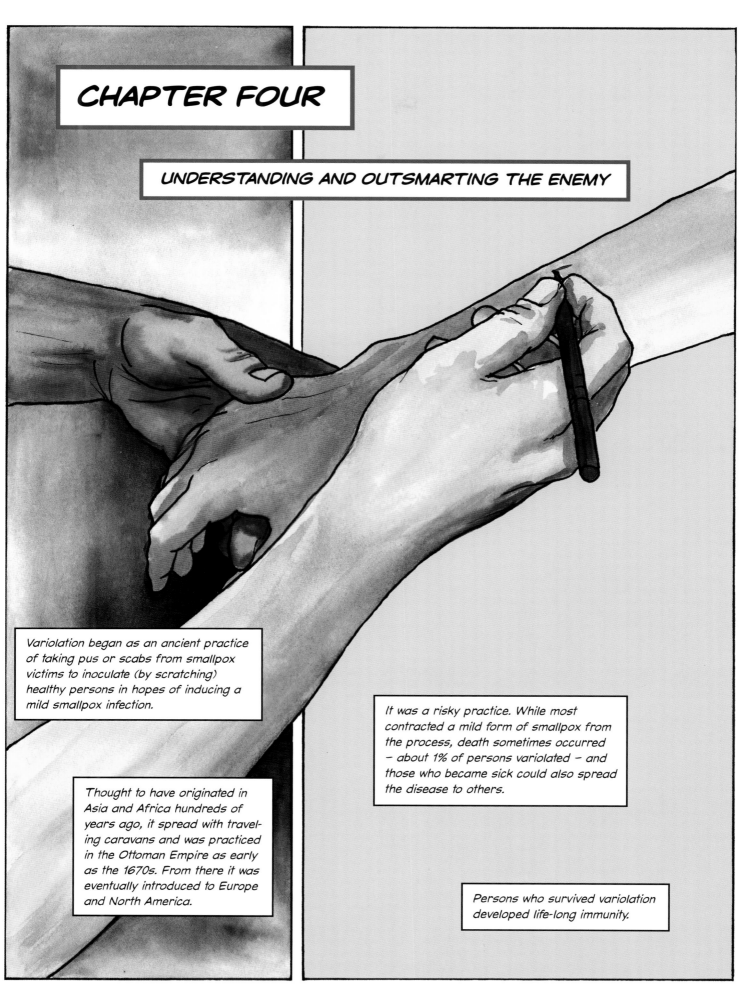

CHAPTER FOUR

UNDERSTANDING AND OUTSMARTING THE ENEMY

Variolation began as an ancient practice of taking pus or scabs from smallpox victims to inoculate (by scratching) healthy persons in hopes of inducing a mild smallpox infection.

It was a risky practice. While most contracted a mild form of smallpox from the process, death sometimes occurred – about 1% of persons variolated – and those who became sick could also spread the disease to others.

Thought to have originated in Asia and Africa hundreds of years ago, it spread with traveling caravans and was practiced in the Ottoman Empire as early as the 1670s. From there it was eventually introduced to Europe and North America.

Persons who survived variolation developed life-long immunity.

Early in the 17th century people became aware of how smallpox might spread and how to avoid it.

Separating sick persons was a practice found even among isolated tribes in all parts of the world.

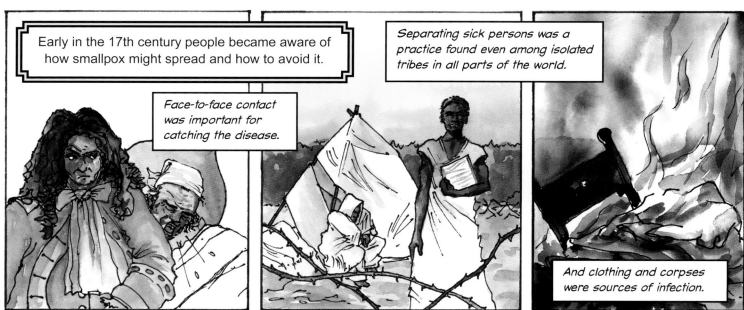

Face-to-face contact was important for catching the disease.

And clothing and corpses were sources of infection.

The Spread of Variolation

In 1716, Lady Mary Montague, wife of the British Ambassador to Turkey, saw variolation and promoted its use in England some 70 years before Jenner's discovery of cowpox and vaccination.

Understanding smallpox's transmission had its dark side also . . .

COLONEL AMHERST:
"Could it not be contrived to send smallpox among these disaffected tribes of Indians? We must on this occasion use every stratagem in our power to reduce them."

BOUQUET:
"I will try to inoculate them with some blankets that may fall in their hands, and take care not to get the disease myself."

During the Boston smallpox epidemics of 1721, Cotton Mather noted that whites suffered more than blacks – who had brought variolation from Africa.

That same year, a ship docked in Boston and introduced smallpox to the 11,000 residents. Within six months, 6,000 had become ill.

In 1776, an American colonial army that was planning to attack Quebec, retreated when a smallpox epidemic broke out in the city.

In 1777, after the failed attempt on Quebec, General Washington persuaded Congress to variolate members of the military in the American colonies.

Likewise 100 years later In 1870, during the Franco-Prussian war in Europe, the French, whose soldiers were not vaccinated, lost 23,400 soldiers.

But the Germans, who were vaccinated, only lost 278 soldiers to the smallpox epidemics raging at the time.

Debates over the safety and appropriateness of variolation continued into the 19th century. By the mid 18th century, smallpox was found everywhere in the world except Australia and several small islands in the Pacific.
But in 1789, and again 1829, smallpox was introduced into Australia and devastated the Aborigines. Both epidemics quickly died out.

The Age of Vaccination is Born

In 1796, English physician Edward Jenner noted that milkmaids retained their fair skin and complexion and seldom had pockmarks or scars like the rest of the population. This implied that milkmaids had developed a level of immunity to smallpox.

He decided to test the common lore that milkmaids never contracted smallpox.

Jenner experimented by using material from a blister of a milkmaid (cowpox) to induce a mild smallpox-like re-action in a young boy named James Phipps on May 14, 1796.

Dr. Jenner later challenged the boy by inoculating him with material from a smallpox patient. The boy did not develop the disease. He had immunity induced by the cowpox inoculation.

Cowpox inoculation material is also known as vaccinia virus.

When he inoculated people with cowpox material who had not had smallpox before and who were not working with cows, Jenner noticed the patients developed a small pustular wound that eventually healed and gave them protection or immunity from smallpox.

Jenner was the first to use cowpox. Others before him had long used the actual smallpox material to inoculate others by **variolation**. **Vaccination** takes its name from the Latin word for cow, "vacca," reflecting its roots in Jenner's experimentation with cowpox.

Jenner's former home, The Chantry, is now a museum.

It is even known that the cow from which much of Dr. Jenner's cowpox material was gathered was called Blossom. Her hide has long been on display at the St. Georges Hospital Medical Library in England.

In contrast to variolation, Jenner provided a safer protective option by using the cowpox virus (*vaccinia* virus), a cousin of the smallpox virus, which led to immunity and generally did not cause sickness or death.

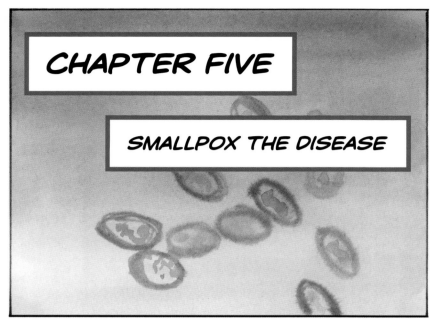

CHAPTER FIVE

SMALLPOX THE DISEASE

There are two types of smallpox virus. One is called *variola major* and kills 30% of its victims. The other type, *variola minor*, is less severe and kills only 1–2%. The word *variola* is Latin for "spotted."

INCUBATION PERIOD, APPROX. 14 DAYS, USUALLY 10–14 DAYS

| 1 | 2 | 3 | 4 | 5 | 6 | 7 | 8 | 9 | 10 | 11 | 12 | 13 | 14 | 15 | 16 | 17 | 18 | 19 |

INITIAL INFECTION

ONSET OF SYMPTOMS

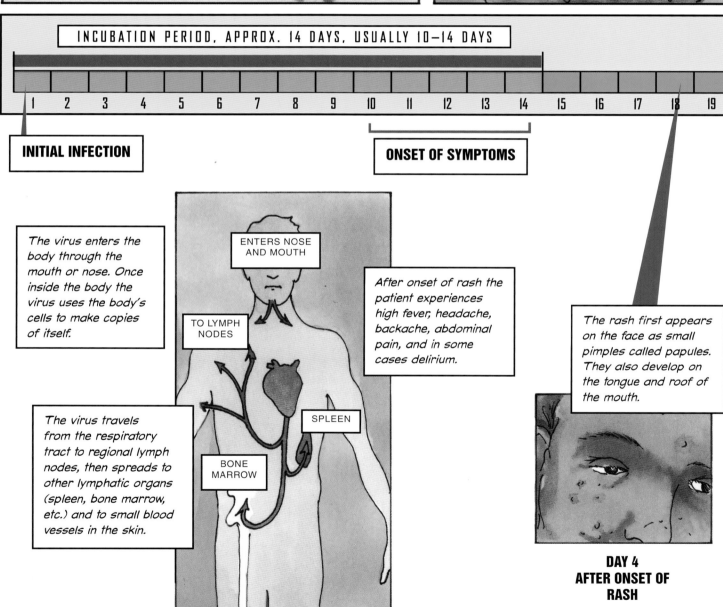

ENTERS NOSE AND MOUTH

TO LYMPH NODES

SPLEEN

BONE MARROW

The virus enters the body through the mouth or nose. Once inside the body the virus uses the body's cells to make copies of itself.

The virus travels from the respiratory tract to regional lymph nodes, then spreads to other lymphatic organs (spleen, bone marrow, etc.) and to small blood vessels in the skin.

After onset of rash the patient experiences high fever, headache, backache, abdominal pain, and in some cases delirium.

The rash first appears on the face as small pimples called papules. They also develop on the tongue and roof of the mouth.

DAY 4 AFTER ONSET OF RASH

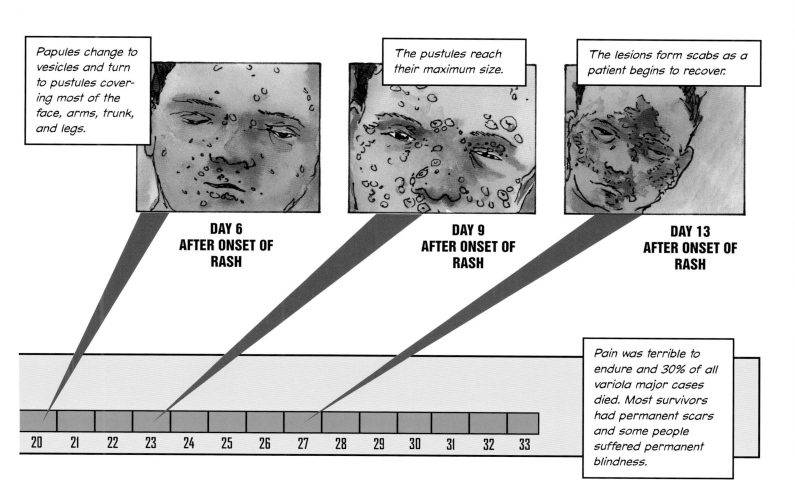

Papules change to vesicles and turn to pustules covering most of the face, arms, trunk, and legs.

DAY 6 AFTER ONSET OF RASH

The pustules reach their maximum size.

DAY 9 AFTER ONSET OF RASH

The lesions form scabs as a patient begins to recover.

DAY 13 AFTER ONSET OF RASH

Pain was terrible to endure and 30% of all variola major cases died. Most survivors had permanent scars and some people suffered permanent blindness.

| 20 | 21 | 22 | 23 | 24 | 25 | 26 | 27 | 28 | 29 | 30 | 31 | 32 | 33 |

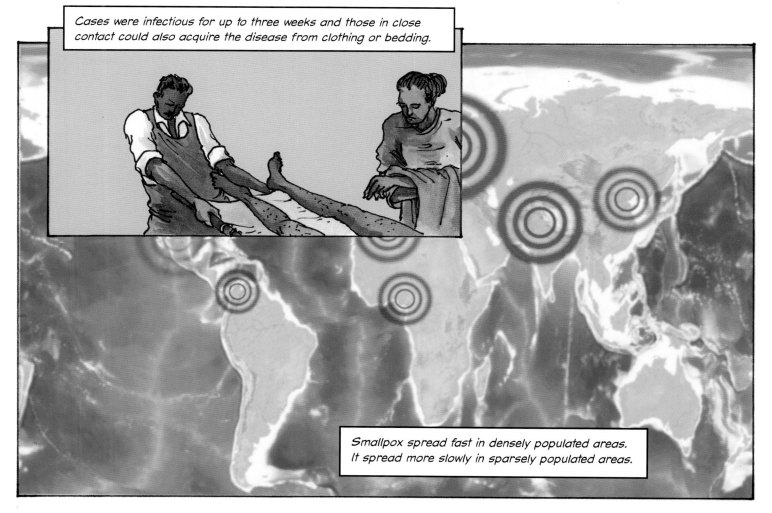

Cases were infectious for up to three weeks and those in close contact could also acquire the disease from clothing or bedding.

Smallpox spread fast in densely populated areas. It spread more slowly in sparsely populated areas.

31

How people protected themselves before modern vaccines . . .

The Jenner vaccinia virus from cowpox could not survive on its own for long. By vaccinating someone and waiting 7–14 days, pustular material from the vaccinated person could be used to vaccinate another person.

Throughout most of the 19th century, the vaccinia virus was sustained by such arm-to-arm vaccinations.

In 1803–1806 on the order of King Charles IV of Spain, vaccinia virus was transferred from Spain to South American colonies. The Captain Balmis-Salvany expedition involved 20 orphans vaccinated arm-to-arm in succession during the long sea voyage to ensure that the vaccinia virus arrived overseas in good shape.

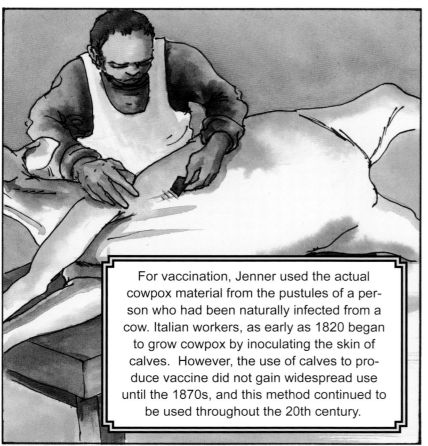

For vaccination, Jenner used the actual cowpox material from the pustules of a person who had been naturally infected from a cow. Italian workers, as early as 1820 began to grow cowpox by inoculating the skin of calves. However, the use of calves to produce vaccine did not gain widespread use until the 1870s, and this method continued to be used throughout the 20th century.

The material for vaccination was unable to be preserved for more than a few days. Therefore, Jenner's discovery was mainly practiced in the capital cities of major countries . . . nevertheless, the arm-to-arm transport of vaccinia virus served colonies and rural areas well.

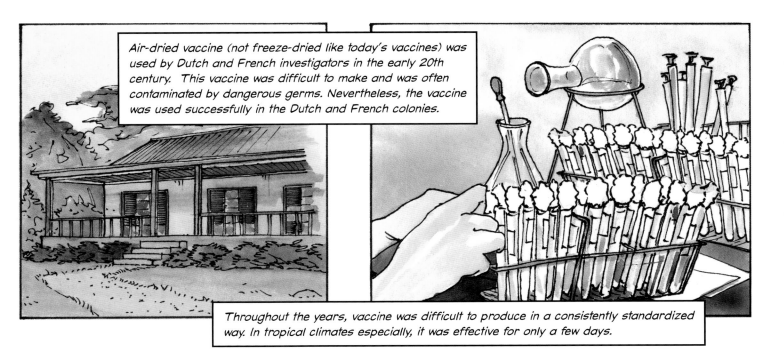

Air-dried vaccine (not freeze-dried like today's vaccines) was used by Dutch and French investigators in the early 20th century. This vaccine was difficult to make and was often contaminated by dangerous germs. Nevertheless, the vaccine was used successfully in the Dutch and French colonies.

Throughout the years, vaccine was difficult to produce in a consistently standardized way. In tropical climates especially, it was effective for only a few days.

In the 1950s, a satisfactory freeze-dried product was developed by Dr. Leslie Collier in the United Kingdom. He showed the vaccine could be kept at 37 degrees Celsius (98.6 degrees Farenheit) for up to four months. Drying by freezing enabled the virus to survive for longer periods, making it much more practical in tropical climates.

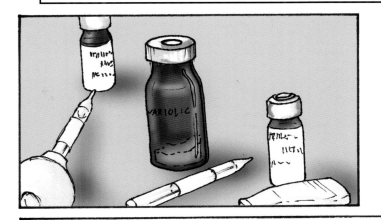

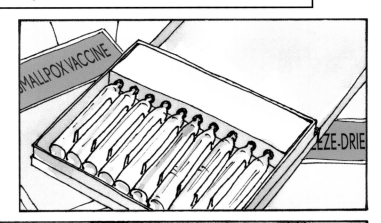

By the 20th century, vaccinia virus (the virus grown on calves and harvested to make vaccine) was more widely available and vaccination was generally well accepted.

CHAPTER SIX

PREPARING THE BATTLE & MUSTERING THE POLITICAL WILL

DR. JENNER'S LEGACY

"In 1796, the English country doctor, Edward Jenner, discovered the principle of vaccination. By 1801 more than 100,000 persons had protected themselves with his vaccine, and he predicted that 'the annihilation of the smallpox — the most dreadful scourge of the human species — must be the final result of this practice.' In the end it took 183 years and a huge international effort, under the aegis of the WHO. But Dr. Jenner was proved right."

Quote from: World Health, The Magazine of the World Health Organization, Aug-Sept 87, pg 16

Early Efforts at Smallpox Control

Throughout the 19th and early 20th centuries, vaccines became available to most countries around the world.

In 1950, the Directing Council of PAHO (Pan American Health Organization – the Regional Office of the World Health Organization) approved smallpox eradication in the Americas.

In 1955, the WHO began a malaria eradication campaign. It depended on DDT to kill mosquitoes that transmitted the infection. But eradication proved to be difficult and the mosquitoes began to be resistant to DDT. The world was skeptical about a new eradication scheme.

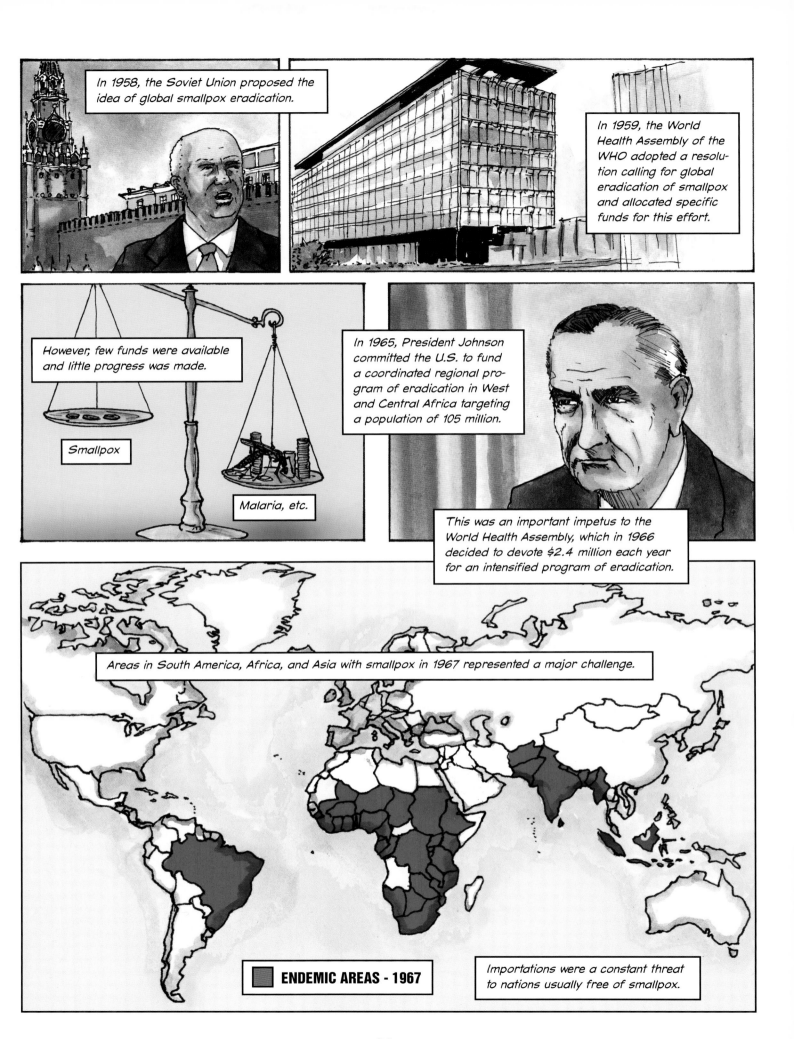

In 1958, the Soviet Union proposed the idea of global smallpox eradication.

In 1959, the World Health Assembly of the WHO adopted a resolution calling for global eradication of smallpox and allocated specific funds for this effort.

However, few funds were available and little progress was made.

Smallpox

Malaria, etc.

In 1965, President Johnson committed the U.S. to fund a coordinated regional program of eradication in West and Central Africa targeting a population of 105 million.

This was an important impetus to the World Health Assembly, which in 1966 decided to devote $2.4 million each year for an intensified program of eradication.

Areas in South America, Africa, and Asia with smallpox in 1967 represented a major challenge.

ENDEMIC AREAS - 1967

Importations were a constant threat to nations usually free of smallpox.

Importations . . .

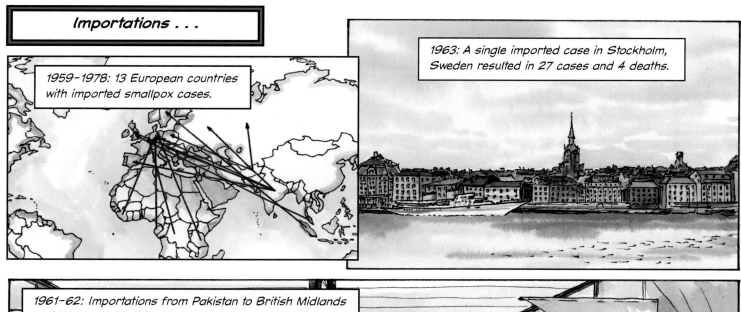

1959–1978: 13 European countries with imported smallpox cases.

1963: A single imported case in Stockholm, Sweden resulted in 27 cases and 4 deaths.

1961–62: Importations from Pakistan to British Midlands and Wales resulted in 60 cases and several deaths. Smallpox spread in hospitals to patients and staff.

Importations into Europe were so frequent that England and Germany equipped special smallpox hospitals to isolate and treat cases.

The largest importations included: USSR (1959-60), UK (1962), Poland (1963), and Yugoslavia (1972). They caused:

46 cases

47 cases

99 cases

175 cases

Jet travel and rapid movements of people steadily increased the likelihood of disease transmission . . .

. . . and all travelers by sea or air since World War II (1940s) needed vaccination certificates attesting to smallpox vaccination within the preceding 3 years.

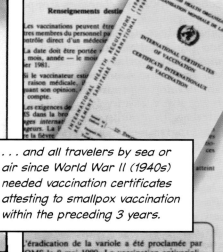

Smallpox spreads in England disease rears its ugly head

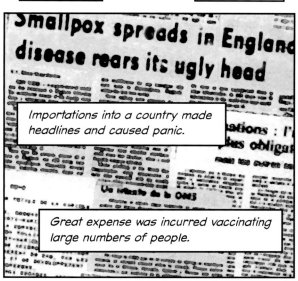

Importations into a country made headlines and caused panic.

Great expense was incurred vaccinating large numbers of people.

Smallpox vaccine was generally safe. Millions of doses were given but some serious side effects occurred. Children with eczema sometimes developed extensive rashes requiring hospitalization. Other side effects could also be serious, but it was a small price to pay to prevent a disease killing 3 out of 10 victims.

In the early 1960s, fewer countries reported smallpox. But eradication progress was slow. Undertaking global eradication became more urgent.

In 1966, 43 countries reported smallpox cases. 31 of these countries − with a total population of one billion − were reporting more than 2.5 million deaths annually.

The World Health Assembly, at its annual meeting of the world's health ministers, voted in 1966 to undertake a special intensified global smallpox eradication campaign. A smallpox eradication unit was created in Geneva.

By 1969, only 18 countries were still endemic. Zaire, Ethiopia, Indonesia, Afghanistan, India, and East and West Pakistan were the major problem areas.

New Tools for Fighting Smallpox

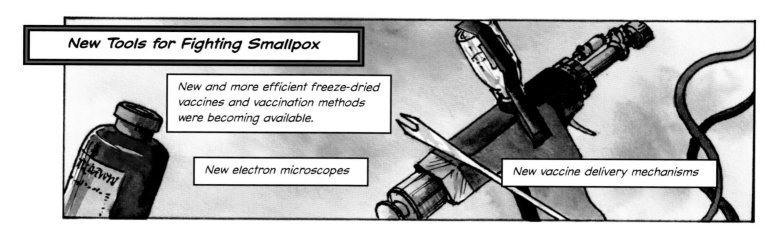

New and more efficient freeze-dried vaccines and vaccination methods were becoming available.

New electron microscopes

New vaccine delivery mechanisms

With the necessity for vaccinating large numbers of people in the remaining endemic countries, new and better techniques for rapidly vaccinating millions were needed.

In the past, French factory workers using a pressure grease gun complained that they often accidentally injected themselves. This may have been the inspiration for the Ped-O-Jet injector.

1890

1963

A foot-powered jet injector (Ped-O-Jet) developed by the U.S. military, was tested in Brazil, Jamaica, Tonga, and the USA for civilian use in 1963-1965. This gun-like injector enabled one person to give as many as a thousand vaccinations per hour without having to rely on electricity. The Ped-O-Jet was easily portable and eliminated the need for needles.

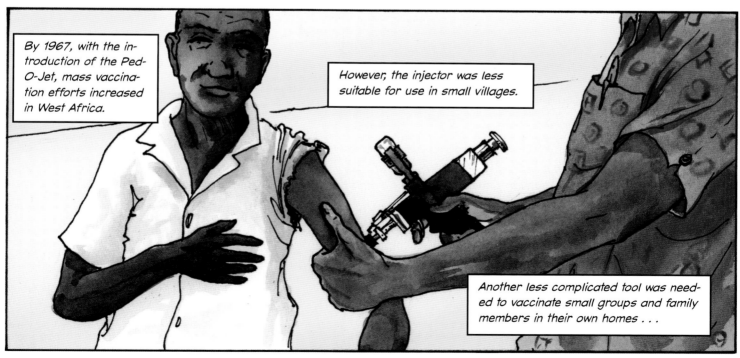

By 1967, with the introduction of the Ped-O-Jet, mass vaccination efforts increased in West Africa.

However, the injector was less suitable for use in small villages.

Another less complicated tool was needed to vaccinate small groups and family members in their own homes . . .

A Very Simple but Revolutionary New Tool

... the Bifurcated Needle – the tool that made all the difference – was invented soon after the Ped-O-Jet injector.

This new tool allowed almost any person to give vaccinations safely.

It was invented by Ben Rubin, a scientist at Wyeth Laboratories during the 1960s. Wyeth granted the WHO free license for its use in the eradication program.

The city of Philadelphia awarded Rubin the John Scott Medal, one of the most prestigious awards for an inventor.

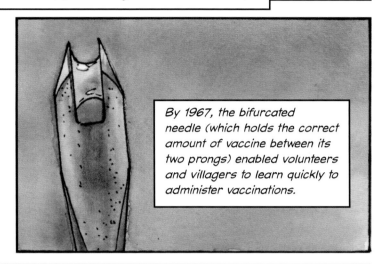

By 1967, the bifurcated needle (which holds the correct amount of vaccine between its two prongs) enabled volunteers and villagers to learn quickly to administer vaccinations.

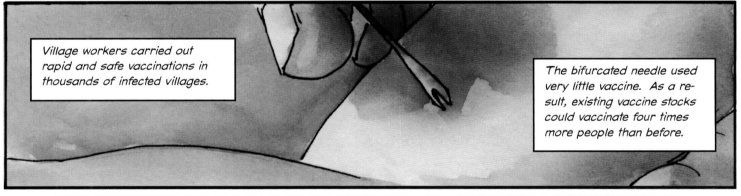

Village workers carried out rapid and safe vaccinations in thousands of infected villages.

The bifurcated needle used very little vaccine. As a result, existing vaccine stocks could vaccinate four times more people than before.

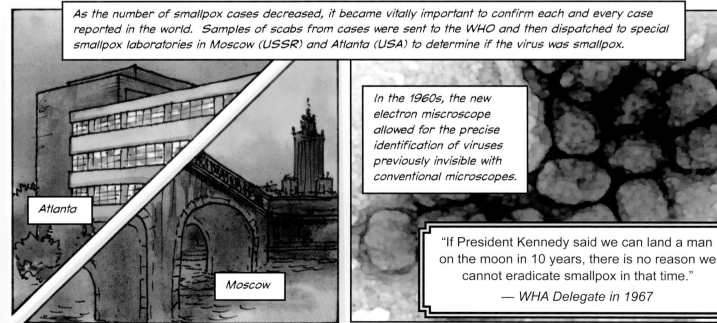

As the number of smallpox cases decreased, it became vitally important to confirm each and every case reported in the world. Samples of scabs from cases were sent to the WHO and then dispatched to special smallpox laboratories in Moscow (USSR) and Atlanta (USA) to determine if the virus was smallpox.

Atlanta

Moscow

In the 1960s, the new electron miscroscope allowed for the precise identification of viruses previously invisible with conventional microscopes.

"If President Kennedy said we can land a man on the moon in 10 years, there is no reason we cannot eradicate smallpox in that time."
— WHA Delegate in 1967

39

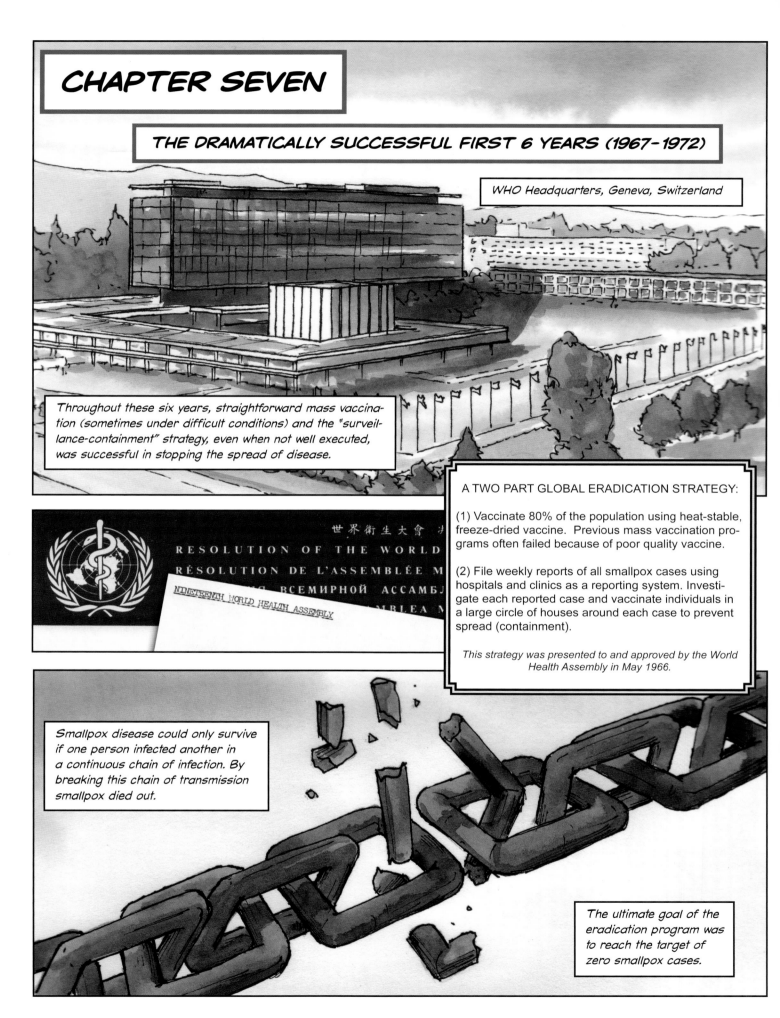

CHAPTER SEVEN

THE DRAMATICALLY SUCCESSFUL FIRST 6 YEARS (1967–1972)

WHO Headquarters, Geneva, Switzerland

Throughout these six years, straightforward mass vaccination (sometimes under difficult conditions) and the "surveillance-containment" strategy, even when not well executed, was successful in stopping the spread of disease.

RESOLUTION OF THE WORLD
RÉSOLUTION DE L'ASSEMBLÉE M
ВСЕМИРНОЙ АССАМБ
NINETEENTH WORLD HEALTH ASSEMBLY

A TWO PART GLOBAL ERADICATION STRATEGY:

(1) Vaccinate 80% of the population using heat-stable, freeze-dried vaccine. Previous mass vaccination programs often failed because of poor quality vaccine.

(2) File weekly reports of all smallpox cases using hospitals and clinics as a reporting system. Investigate each reported case and vaccinate individuals in a large circle of houses around each case to prevent spread (containment).

This strategy was presented to and approved by the World Health Assembly in May 1966.

Smallpox disease could only survive if one person infected another in a continuous chain of infection. By breaking this chain of transmission smallpox died out.

The ultimate goal of the eradication program was to reach the target of zero smallpox cases.

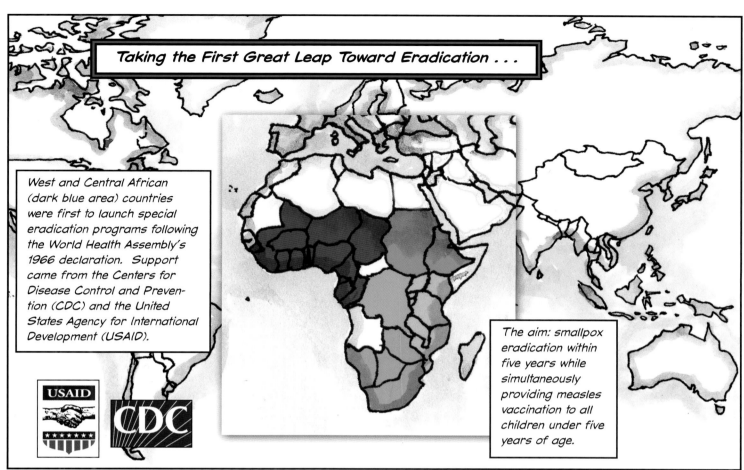

Taking the First Great Leap Toward Eradication . . .

West and Central African (dark blue area) countries were first to launch special eradication programs following the World Health Assembly's 1966 declaration. Support came from the Centers for Disease Control and Prevention (CDC) and the United States Agency for International Development (USAID).

The aim: smallpox eradication within five years while simultaneously providing measles vaccination to all children under five years of age.

At that time some countries (Sierra Leone, Dahomey – now Benin) had the highest rates of smallpox in the world, with very limited infrastructure and resources.

It took 3 1/2 years to eradicate smallpox in the 20 countries of West and Central Africa . . .

. . . almost two years ahead of schedule and under budget using only 32 of 47 million U.S. dollars allocated by USAID.

West African smallpox eradication posters in local languages

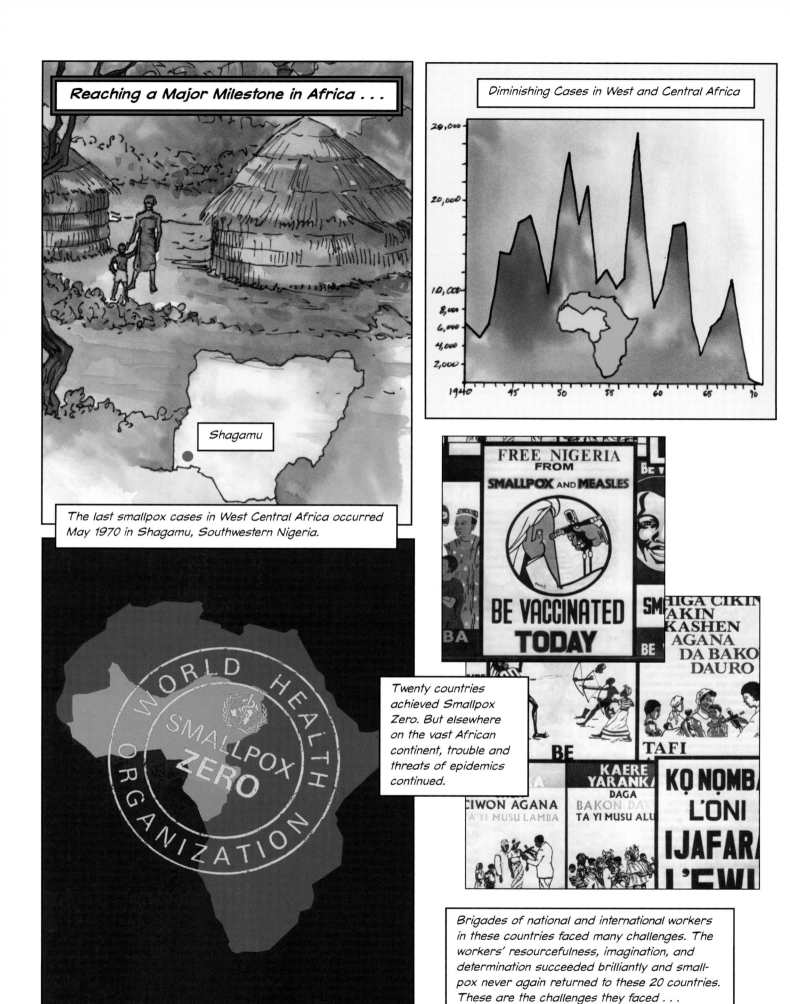

Reaching a Major Milestone in Africa . . .

Shagamu

The last smallpox cases in West Central Africa occurred May 1970 in Shagamu, Southwestern Nigeria.

Diminishing Cases in West and Central Africa

WORLD HEALTH ORGANIZATION
SMALLPOX ZERO

FREE NIGERIA FROM SMALLPOX AND MEASLES
BE VACCINATED TODAY

Twenty countries achieved Smallpox Zero. But elsewhere on the vast African continent, trouble and threats of epidemics continued.

Brigades of national and international workers in these countries faced many challenges. The workers' resourcefulness, imagination, and determination succeeded brilliantly and smallpox never again returned to these 20 countries. These are the challenges they faced . . .

Armies of workers overcame tropical heat, monsoon rains, enormous personal and logistical challenges to vaccinate their populations and to find and stop outbreaks of smallpox.

Challenge #1 Reaching the People

Every mode of transportation was used . . .

Four-wheel-drive vehicles for bad roads, desert tracks, and cross country paths; motorbikes and bicycles for trekking on foot-paths and going house-to-house to search for cases and perform containment vaccinations.

Challenge #2 Taboos, Voodoo, Religious Beliefs

There was mild opposition to vaccination in some areas based on the cultural worship of the god of smallpox, Shapona.

Fetisheurs were believed to have special power over smallpox. Some fetisheurs used smallpox material to variolate.

By custom the fetisheurs inherited all the possessions of dead smallpox victims and as such they had little incentive to participate in the eradication of smallpox.

As smallpox disappeared, it was reported that some fetisheurs were substituting chickenpox (a generally mild disease) as the focus of their rituals and "income."

Challenge #3 Fear of the Ped-O-Jet Injector and the Tax Man

A single Ped-O-Jet injector could successfully administer up to a thousand vaccinations per hour. Sometimes it frightened villagers because it resembled a gun.

In 1967 in Ibadan, Nigeria, one of Africa's largest cities, more than 750,000 smallpox vaccinations were given in 10 days using Ped-O-Jet injectors.

Vaccination workers were so well organized that many villagers thought they were tax collectors from the government and some villagers even fled.

44

Challenge #4 Wars, Conflicts, and Refugees

Cease fires during conflicts and wars were a necessary and a positive outcome of the eradication program.

One of the first cease fires was in Biafra (1967) when the Nigerian government in Lagos, Nigeria, sent vaccines to Biafra to protect its population.

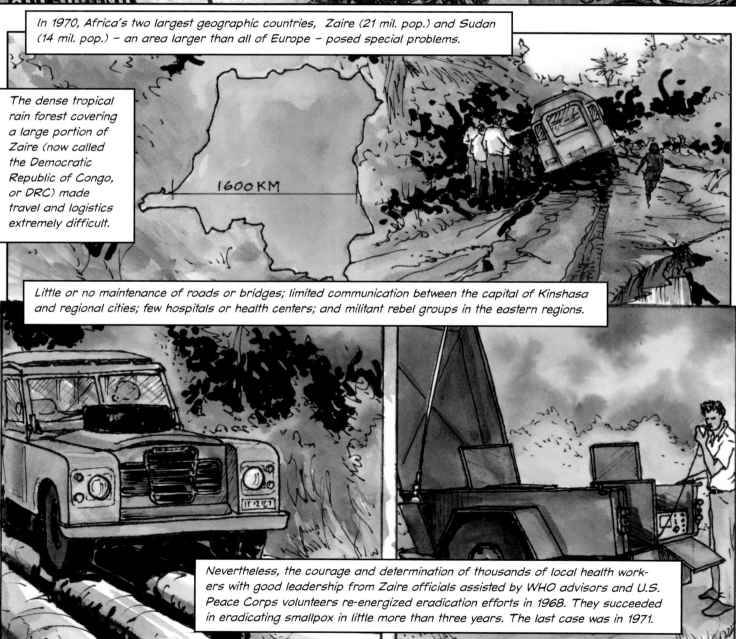

In 1970, Africa's two largest geographic countries, Zaire (21 mil. pop.) and Sudan (14 mil. pop.) – an area larger than all of Europe – posed special problems.

The dense tropical rain forest covering a large portion of Zaire (now called the Democratic Republic of Congo, or DRC) made travel and logistics extremely difficult.

1600KM

Little or no maintenance of roads or bridges; limited communication between the capital of Kinshasa and regional cities; few hospitals or health centers; and militant rebel groups in the eastern regions.

Nevertheless, the courage and determination of thousands of local health workers with good leadership from Zaire officials assisted by WHO advisors and U.S. Peace Corps volunteers re-energized eradication efforts in 1968. They succeeded in eradicating smallpox in little more than three years. The last case was in 1971.

Sudan had been free of smallpox since 1963, when in 1968 smallpox spread from Ethiopia to Sudan. Epidemics of variola minor once again afflicted the country.

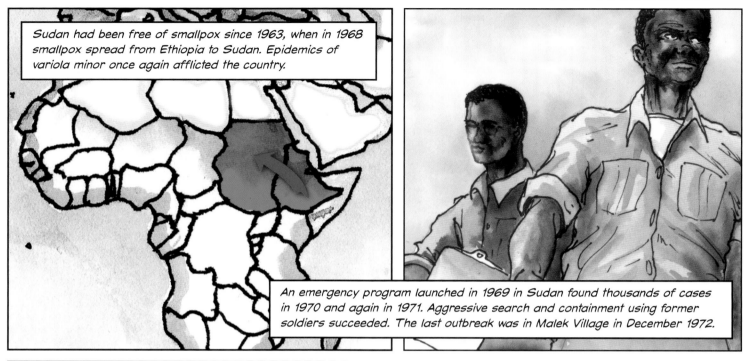

An emergency program launched in 1969 in Sudan found thousands of cases in 1970 and again in 1971. Aggressive search and containment using former soldiers succeeded. The last outbreak was in Malek Village in December 1972.

An importation from South Africa was a major setback in Botswana, where the last cases were reported in January 1971. By June 1971, Botswana reported hundreds and then thousands of cases.

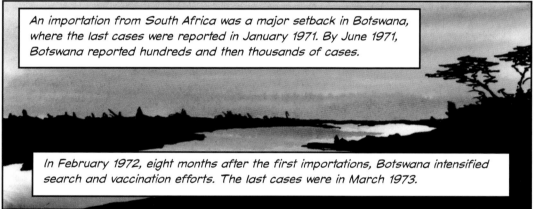

In February 1972, eight months after the first importations, Botswana intensified search and vaccination efforts. The last cases were in March 1973.

"No program had ever endeavored to accomplish a task as ambitious and overwhelming as this. By 1970, Zaire and Sudan appeared the biggest challenges and by 1972 all countries in Africa were free except for Ethiopia and Botswana."

Quote from D.A. Henderson

And now most of Africa was free of the loathsome smallpox . . . except for Ethiopia. This epic last struggle in Ethiopia is described in the next chapter.

Countries on other continents succeeded in interrupting smallpox during these first six years (1967–1972) . . .

Brazil . . .

. . . Indonesia . . .

. . . and Afghanistan.

South America

Only Brazil had smallpox in 1966.

100,000,000

The introduction of the Ped-O-Jet injector to Brazil in 1967 helped convince Brazil and PAHO that eradicating smallpox was now possible in a population of 100 million.

From 1967 to 1971, thousands of workers vaccinated 94 million Brazilians.

How did they do it?

Weekly and monthly surveillance bulletins gave health workers up-to-date information on where smallpox cases were occurring in Brazil.

This timely information increased competition to reach zero cases.

In 1969, surveillance and containment was first introduced in a state of seven million people. By finding each case and by vaccinating in all houses around it, epidemic smallpox was stopped after only 50,000 vaccinations.

In 1971, Brazil reported its last case.

smallpox target zero

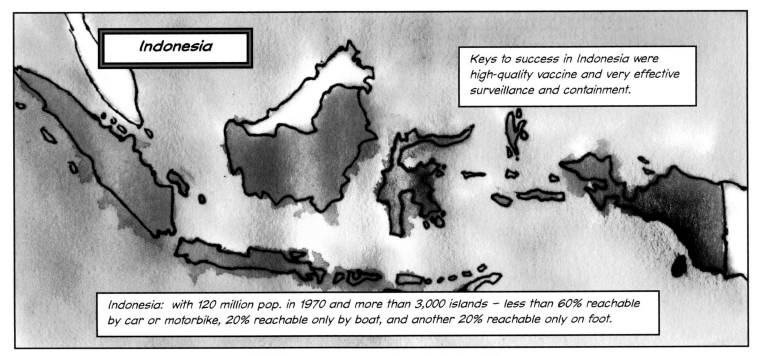

Indonesia

Keys to success in Indonesia were high-quality vaccine and very effective surveillance and containment.

Indonesia: with 120 million pop. in 1970 and more than 3,000 islands – less than 60% reachable by car or motorbike, 20% reachable only by boat, and another 20% reachable only on foot.

Indonesia was free of smallpox from 1937 to 1947.

Smallpox was re-introduced in 1947 and epidemics persisted until 1972.

Hundreds of thousands of cases occurred, many in isolated areas reached only by foot or by boats.

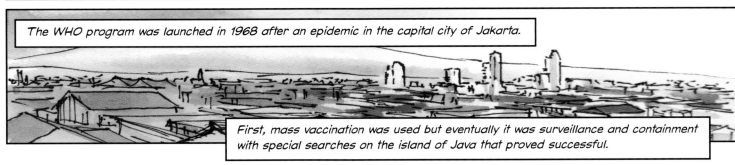

The WHO program was launched in 1968 after an epidemic in the capital city of Jakarta.

First, mass vaccination was used but eventually it was surveillance and containment with special searches on the island of Java that proved successful.

A local health worker in Indonesia made a key discovery. Using a postcard-like picture of a person with smallpox made it easier to find out from schoolchildren where cases were occurring. The pictures of smallpox were so helpful that WHO produced thousands of these small-pox recognition cards. These cards were used successfully in schools, markets, trains, and streets in India, Pakistan and other countries.

By the time the last case occurred in 1972, Indonesia had spent only $1.3 million on the program, or one U.S. cent per person. This was one of the most cost effective programs of all the eradication efforts!

Afghanistan

20,000 rural villages at altitudes of more than 1,500 meters with very few people ever vaccinated.

The eradication program began in 1963 with fewer than 500,000 vaccinations performed by 1969 . . . smallpox persisted.

Under new and dedicated leadership and a courageous and industrious national staff, assisted in part by women Peace Corps volunteers, a well-organized country-wide vaccination campaign succeeded in reaching more than 80% of the population.

Special education efforts were needed to reach women and their children in many rural areas where women could not leave their homes and male vaccinators were forbidden to enter.

Afghanistan had one of the most effective programs of the entire global campaign.

With good surveillance and containment, cases decreased to 750 in 1970 then to less than 250 cases in 1971 with the last case in September 1972.

But this was no time to rest . . .

. . . considering Pakistan's many epidemics just across the border and with massive epidemics in India and East Pakistan (now Bangladesh).

By 1973, India, Pakistan, Nepal, and Bangladesh, along with Ethiopia, became the final assault in the campaign to achieve Global Smallpox Target Zero.

CHAPTER EIGHT

THE FINAL VICTORY – SMALLPOX ZERO

1973–1978, the last six years: an epic struggle to stop smallpox in the last six infected countries.

India, Bangladesh, Nepal, and Pakistan had large mobile populations.

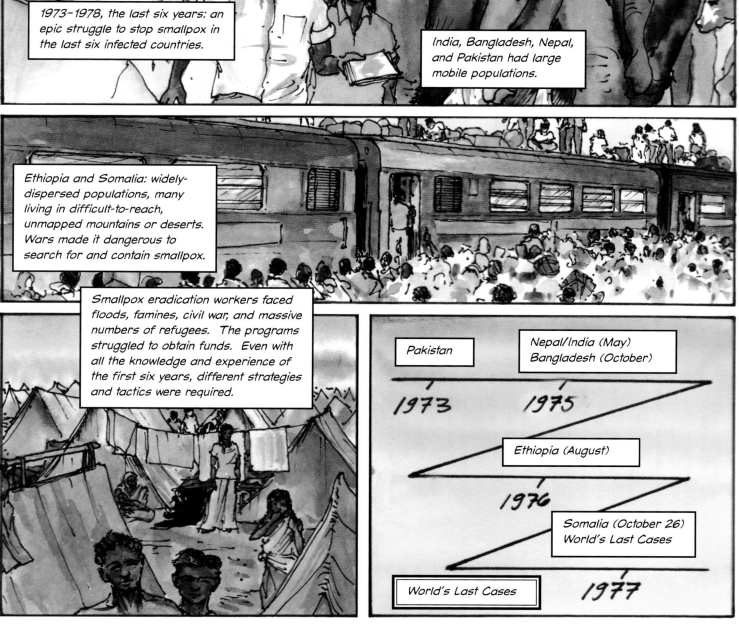

Ethiopia and Somalia: widely-dispersed populations, many living in difficult-to-reach, unmapped mountains or deserts. Wars made it dangerous to search for and contain smallpox.

Smallpox eradication workers faced floods, famines, civil war, and massive numbers of refugees. The programs struggled to obtain funds. Even with all the knowledge and experience of the first six years, different strategies and tactics were required.

Pakistan

Nepal/India (May)
Bangladesh (October)

1973

1975

Ethiopia (August)

1976

Somalia (October 26)
World's Last Cases

World's Last Cases

1977

The last six countries declared national emergencies to confront the smallpox epidemics. Eradicating smallpox was in doubt several times: at least twice in India, several times in Bangladesh and Ethiopia, and during the final Somalia effort.

National health workers were joined by smallpox veterans from the earlier, successful country eradication efforts.

Around the world, some people questioned whether it was possible to reach Smallpox Zero.

smallpox target (zero)

New Leadership at the WHO

Dr. Halfdan Mahler, a Danish physician and tuberculosis expert, became the WHO Director-General in 1973. He strongly supported smallpox eradication and greatly strengthened the WHO support.

Lessons Learned from Earlier Smallpox Epidemics Contributed to its Demise . . .

RING VACCINATION Once cases were found, all family and visitors to and from the villages were vaccinated to prevent the disease spreading further. Thus, a ring of protection was established and maintained.

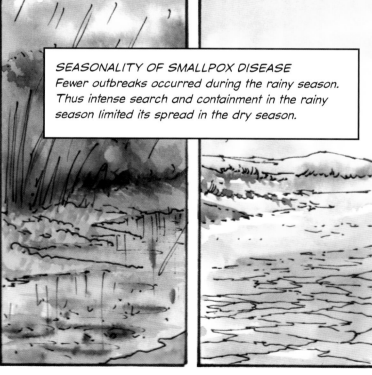

SEASONALITY OF SMALLPOX DISEASE Fewer outbreaks occurred during the rainy season. Thus intense search and containment in the rainy season limited its spread in the dry season.

India 1966-1975: An Incredible Smallpox Eradication Saga

- A country of immense size and vast population estimated at 550 million in 1970. With 80% of the population in rural areas
- Large movements of people: funerals, marriages, pilgrimages, job seekers, beggars
- 10,800 trains each day moved 10 million people; extensive road systems with many buses
- Persons sick with smallpox often returned to their home villages infecting people along the way
- Belief that smallpox was the wrath of the goddess Sitala Mata – some resisted vaccination

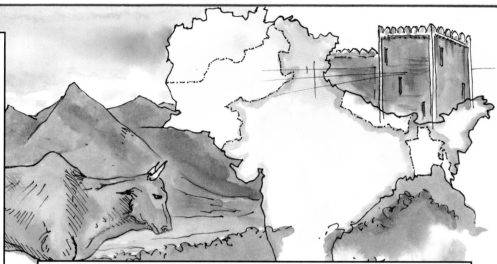

India established its first eradication goal in June 1962. More than 400 million vaccinations were performed. But many cases continued to occur.

Searching for cases continued using the recognition card.

From 1964 to 1966, 30,000 to 40,000 cases occurred each year.

In 1967, more than 84,000 cases occurred and India intensified its smallpox eradication program using new tools including:

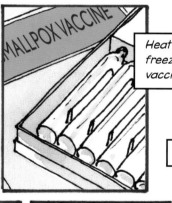

Heat resistant freeze-dried vaccine.

The bifurcated needle.

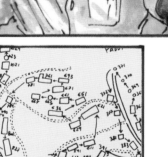

150,000 dedicated Indian health workers.

Improved reporting of cases with rapid containment.

Increased financial support from the WHO and the Swedish International Development Agency (SIDA).

Rapid village-by-village and later house-to-house active searches found many new outbreaks.

And by 1970, cases were down to 12,773.

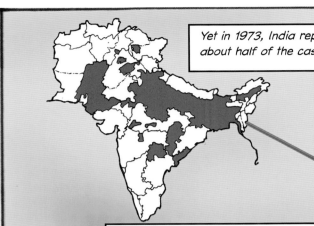

Yet in 1973, India reported 49,000 smallpox cases – about half of the cases reported in the world.

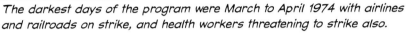

1974 was even worse, with 8,700 outbreaks and more than 116,000 smallpox cases. India mobilized large numbers of health workers to find and contain smallpox during the 1974 monsoon season.

This epidemic surge was most discouraging.

The darkest days of the program were March to April 1974 with airlines and railroads on strike, and health workers threatening to strike also.

HELP FIGHT SMALLPOX take VACCINATION

Tata Industries provided staff and vehicles to help control a very large outbreak centered on the railway station in the major industrial city of Jamshedpur in southern Bihar State.

To stop smallpox, all railway passengers were vaccinated and vaccination check-points were set up in the city. In two months this outbreak was over.

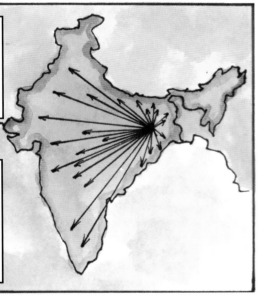

Searches were intensified, especially in markets. A cash reward for reporting smallpox was widely advertised.

In January 1975, with only 230 outbreaks, India launched Operation – Smallpox Zero.

OX

ZERO

On May 18, 1975, the last smallpox case in India was found in the state of Assam. She was Saiban Bihi, a 30-year-old homeless Bangladeshi woman who had been sleeping in a railway station.

But 4,500 tickets were sold to passengers going to more than 68 different towns and cities and some of them may have been infected. Unprecedented searches and vaccinations were carried out in these towns and cities. . . no other case was ever found.

After the last case, the reward for reporting a smallpox case increased to 1,000 rupees ($125 USDs) – equivalent to four months' salary for a laborer in India.

Thousands of suspect cases were reported and investigated. None turned out to be smallpox.

On August 15, 1975, Prime Minister Indira Ghandi congratulated the people of India on the 28th year of independence and proclaimed that India for the first time in its long history had won freedom from smallpox.

Smallpox Zero – once thought impossible – became a reality.

The Discouraging Smallpox Saga in Bangladesh (formerly East Pakistan)

Until December 1971, Bangladesh was part of Pakistan and known as East Pakistan. East Pakistan stopped smallpox in 1970: with four cases in September 1969, one case in October 1969, and zero cases in 1970.

With the end of the civil war in December 1971, refugees with smallpox disease returned from India. Smallpox was reintroduced to the new nation of Bangladesh.

Smallpox had spread for weeks without being detected in the largest refugee site, Salt Lake Camp, near Calcutta. A doctor in the U.S. saw what looked like people with active smallpox in television reports about the Bangladesh refugees in Salt Lake Camp. The television diagnosis was correct!

By mid-January 1972, more than 2.6 million refugees returning home spread smallpox all around the new nation of Bangladesh.

This was a discouraging set-back for a land once free of smallpox.

Bangladesh presented the ultimate challenge:

- More than 100 million people
- Some of the heaviest monsoons and destructive typhoons in the world
- Major flooding each year displacing millions of population
- Crowded displacements during floods favoring the spread of smallpox
- Country crisscrossed by major rivers making for challenging travel
- Riverboat transportation with its crowded passengers favored spread

Special search programs were initiated. 24,000 workers visited fairs, markets, and houses using a recognition card.

Rewards for reporting smallpox helped find many outbreaks. Intensive containment vaccination stopped smallpox again.

নিকটস্থ স্বাস্থ্য অফিসে গুটি বসন্তের সংবাদ দিয়া

The last case in Bangladesh was in October 1975. This 2-1/2 year-old girl, Rahima Banu, was the last case of the severe type of smallpox (variola major) in the world.

55

The Challenging Smallpox Eradication Saga in Ethiopia

In 1975, after the end of smallpox in Asia, Ethiopia was the only country in the world with known smallpox transmission.

In Ethiopia, only the milder type of smallpox (variola minor) existed. Widely separated mountain villages made it difficult to find cases.

ADDIS ABEBA

Health workers walked or rode mules for days to reach distant mountain villages. Starting in 1974, helicopters made it possible to quickly reach smallpox cases in inaccessible mountain villages.

In 1974, in the midst of the eradication efforts, Emperor Haile Selassie was over-thrown. Widespread fighting hampered eradication efforts.

Smallpox teams with WHO advisers were kidnapped on nine different occasions. The teams were all released after negotiations with government and guerilla groups.

One helicopter and pilot were seized at one point and held for ransom.

Dr. Shafa

We are captured by the Guerillas they want $40 000 Ethiopian dollars for my release or they will kill us

Travel within Ethiopia was highly restricted and health teams were often escorted by the military.

In August 1976, Ethiopia's last outbreak of 16 cases was discovered deep in the Ogaden Desert in the nomadic village of Dimo in Bale. A 3-year-old girl was believed to be the last case of smallpox in the world.

Celebrations to mark the world's last case of smallpox were about to be announced . . .

. . . when a message from the CDC confirmed smallpox in two specimens from Mogadishu, the capital of Somalia.

Smallpox Zero Finally Achieved in Somalia

In the 1970s, Somalia was reported to be well vaccinated and free of smallpox, but the disease was reintroduced in 1976.

Somalia is a desert country. Half of its three million inhabitants are nomads who raise camels and other livestock. The frequent travels to find grazing and water for their animals helped spread smallpox.

Initial investigation of smallpox in Mogadishu suggested the cases had come from an Ethiopian area in the Ogaden Desert. Ethiopia searched wide areas of the desert. No smallpox was found.

Repeated day and night searches of Mogadishu failed to find the sources of the cases.

Then the government carried out a supervised national search and found cases in and around Mogadishu.

57

Somalia declared the epidemic a disaster. The United Nations flew in vehicles and equipment. Additional WHO temporary staff travelled to Somalia. Eventually, more than 1,000 cases were identified and contained.

More cases were found – largely among constantly moving nomad groups.

Finally, October 26, 1977 . . .

. . . Ali Maow Maalin, of Merca, Somalia, was the world's last naturally occurring case of smallpox.

WORLD HEALTH

smallpox is dead!

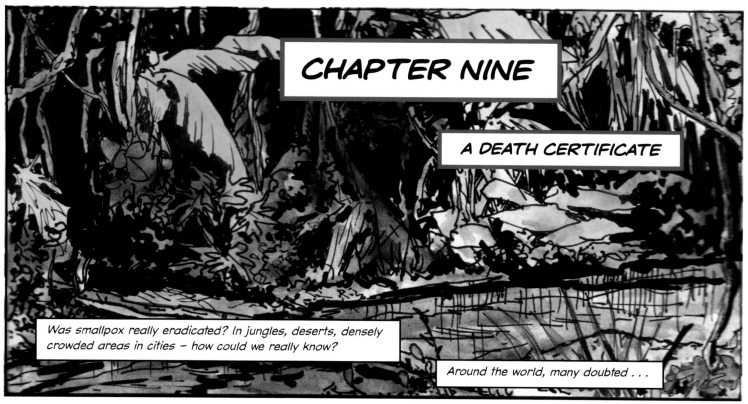

CHAPTER NINE

A DEATH CERTIFICATE

Was smallpox really eradicated? In jungles, deserts, densely crowded areas in cities – how could we really know?

Around the world, many doubted . . .

How could the world prove that Smallpox Zero had been achieved?

Countries repeatedly sent thousands of workers from village-to-village searching for cases of the dreaded disease.

Rewards were offered for the discovery of a case.

Eradication meant a total absence of human cases. Without human cases there could be no circulation of the virus.

For two years after the last confirmed case, the countries carried out active searches for smallpox. Finding even one case would prove that smallpox was still present.

Samples of scabs and pustules from many suspicious cases were sent to the two international WHO Collaborating Reference Laboratories.

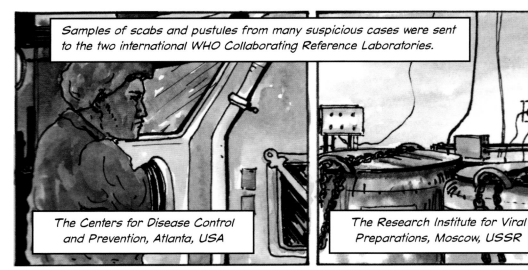

The Centers for Disease Control and Prevention, Atlanta, USA

The Research Institute for Viral Preparations, Moscow, USSR

Between 1977–1980, more than 8,900 samples were sent to the two official laboratories to determine if they contained smallpox.

The laboratories found chickenpox, monkeypox-like diseases, or other viruses. No smallpox virus was found.

After two years of repeated searches, international commissions comprised of national and international experts (many doubted that smallpox was eradicated) visited each country and travelled widely trying to find smallpox.

From 1973 to 1979, 21 independent commissions in 36 countries and special reviews in 79 countries REVEALED NO SMALLPOX CASES.

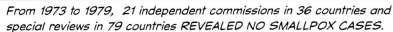

Finding no smallpox cases, each country was officially certified free of smallpox.

Another Possible Threat

The monkeypox and smallpox viruses are closely related. Monkeypox primarily infects small rodents and monkeys in Equatorial African forests. Occasional human monkeypox cases occur. Could monkeypox spread and cause human epidemics?

Study of monkeypox since 1980 has found no evidence it can cause human epidemics.

A Global International Small-pox Commission appointed by the WHO reviewed all of the work that had been done. They determined that the world was free of small-pox. Thus, in May 1980, the World Health Assembly declared the world free of smallpox and recommended smallpox vaccination should cease in all countries.

For seven years after the declaration of global eradication, 1980–1986, the WHO systematically investigated all rumors of smallpox anywhere in the world. No smallpox was found.

Some smallpox virus samples were present in different diagnostic laboratories worldwide . . .

A Tragic Laboratory Accident in 1978

A year after the last naturally occurring smallpox case in Somalia a smallpox case occurred in a research laboratory.

It occurred at a research laboratory in England where a person who had not been vaccinated died after exposure. Smallpox virus had accidentally escaped from a research laboratory.

Fearful of such incidents the WHO:

1. Designated only two officially recognized high security laboratories (Atlanta and Moscow) to store and handle smallpox virus.
2. Requested all national laboratories destroy their smallpox virus samples or transfer them to one of the two official high security laboratories.
3. Created an expert committee to discuss the possibility of eventually destroying the existing specimens held in the two official laboratories (Atlanta and Moscow).

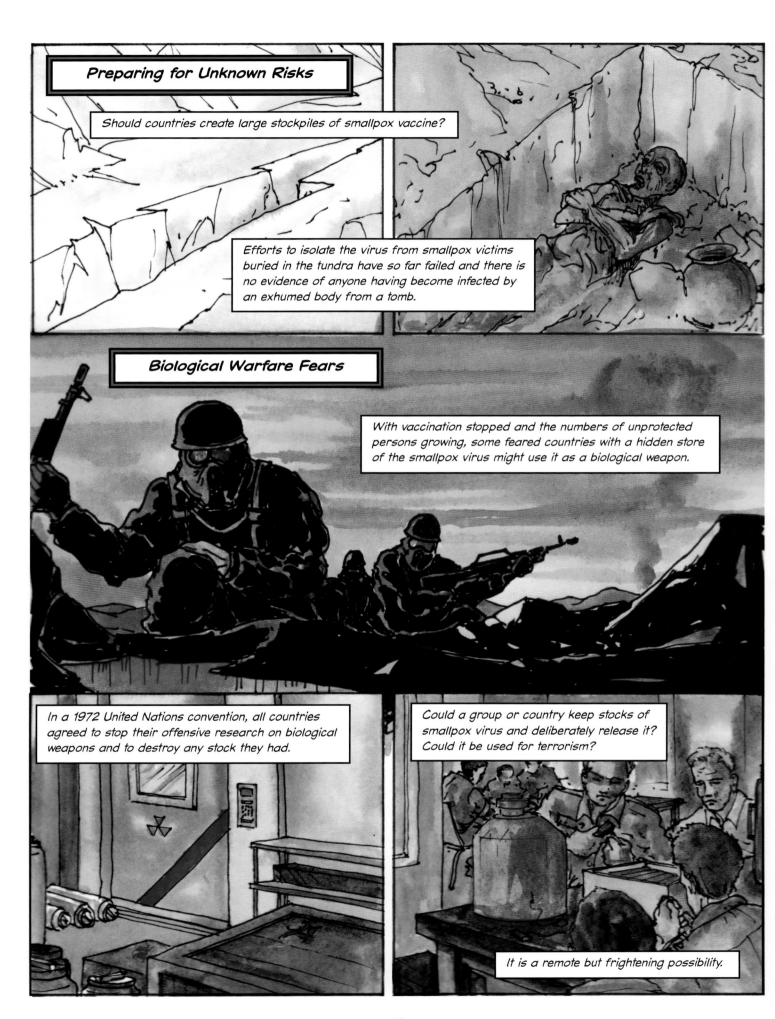

Preparing for Unknown Risks

Should countries create large stockpiles of smallpox vaccine?

Efforts to isolate the virus from smallpox victims buried in the tundra have so far failed and there is no evidence of anyone having become infected by an exhumed body from a tomb.

Biological Warfare Fears

With vaccination stopped and the numbers of unprotected persons growing, some feared countries with a hidden store of the smallpox virus might use it as a biological weapon.

In a 1972 United Nations convention, all countries agreed to stop their offensive research on biological weapons and to destroy any stock they had.

Could a group or country keep stocks of smallpox virus and deliberately release it? Could it be used for terrorism?

It is a remote but frightening possibility.

Final and Decisive Destruction of Smallpox Virus Kept in the Two High Security Labs

The WHO first suggested destruction of all samples as early as 1986. Destruction has not yet occurred.

In 2002, WHO authorized temporary retention of the virus for research and studies at the CDC and the State Research Center of Virology and Biotechnology (VECTOR) in Koltsovo, Russia.

Renewed consideration for destroying the remaining stocks of smallpox virus is planned.. A definitive decision is scheduled for 2011 – after fifteen years of research on the smallpox virus.

Entering the 21st Century

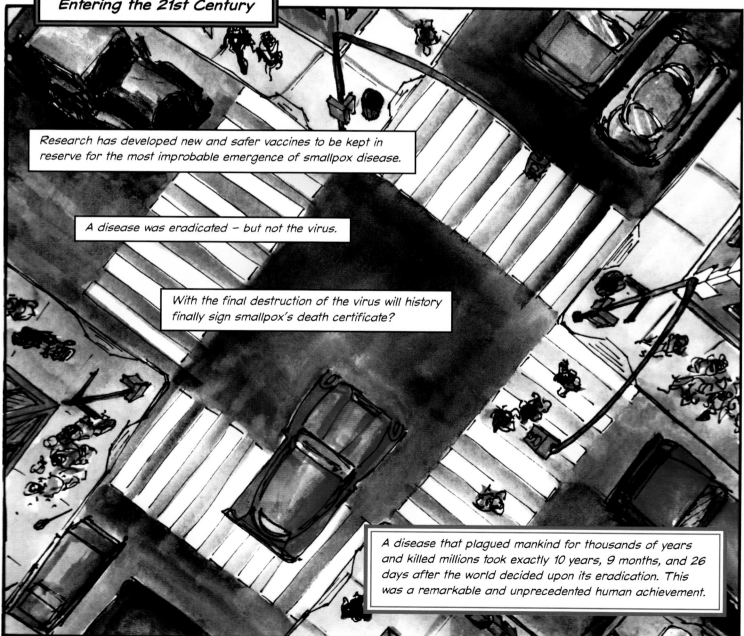

Research has developed new and safer vaccines to be kept in reserve for the most improbable emergence of smallpox disease.

A disease was eradicated – but not the virus.

With the final destruction of the virus will history finally sign smallpox's death certificate?

A disease that plagued mankind for thousands of years and killed millions took exactly 10 years, 9 months, and 26 days after the world decided upon its eradication. This was a remarkable and unprecedented human achievement.

CHAPTER TEN

THE LEGACY OF SMALLPOX ERADICATION

Smallpox eradication stimulated a number of new disease control programs.

The public health workers who helped end smallpox were energized and looked for other important public health problems to solve.

In 1974, the WHO launched a new initiative, the Expanded Programme on Immunizations. The success and relatively low cost of smallpox eradication inspired a global effort to dramatically expand the use of safe and effective vaccines.

The Expanded Programme on Immunizations (EPI)

The EPI is credited with saving millions of children's lives. Vaccines to prevent diphtheria, tetanus, pertussis, poliomyelitis, measles and yellow fever are now widely available globally.

To learn about the successes of the EPI go to:
http://www.who.int/immunization_delivery/en/

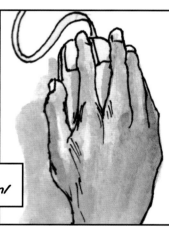

Early Polio Eradication Efforts

Smallpox eradication veterans helped launch the EPI in the Americas, and set the goal of polio eradication.

PAHO launched the EPI in 1977, its polio eradication in 1985, and recorded its last polio cases in 1991.

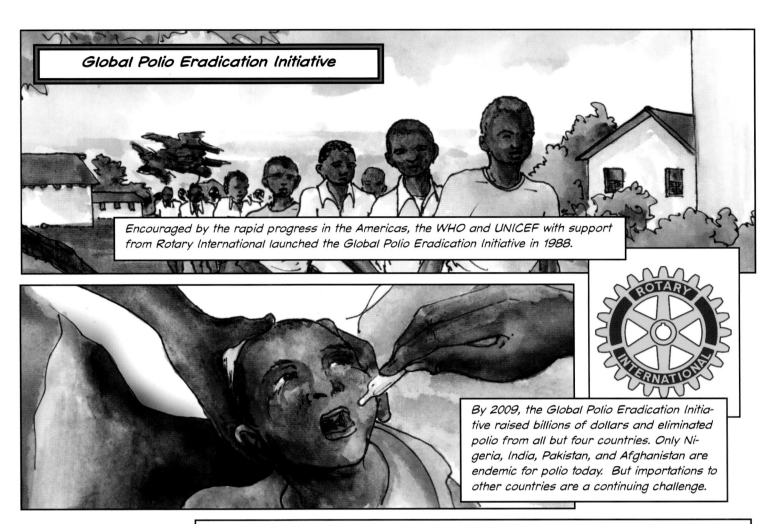

Global Polio Eradication Initiative

Encouraged by the rapid progress in the Americas, the WHO and UNICEF with support from Rotary International launched the Global Polio Eradication Initiative in 1988.

By 2009, the Global Polio Eradication Initiative raised billions of dollars and eliminated polio from all but four countries. Only Nigeria, India, Pakistan, and Afghanistan are endemic for polio today. But importations to other countries are a continuing challenge.

Worldwide, polio cases have dropped an impressive 99%. Will polio be the next disease to be eradicated from planet earth? For more info go to: **http://www.polioeradication.org/**

Guinea Worm Eradication

In 1986, smallpox veterans launched a program to eradicate Guinea worm disease from Africa and Asia.

An estimated 3.5 million people had Guinea worm disease in 20 nations in Africa and Asia.

The Guinea worm is a thin, thread-like worm that can grow as long as a meter. It grows under the skin of the affected person and causes great pain when it emerges through the skin. It is spread by drinking contaminated water. It is so painful it is sometimes called the "fiery serpent."

Only six African nations (Sudan, Ghana, Mali, Ethiopia, Nigeria, Niger) harbored Guinea worm disease in 2009. Since 1986, the number of people infected has been reduced by an impressive 99.7%.

To learn about Guinea Worm Eradication go to:
http://www.cartercenter.org/health/guinea_worm/index.html

The International Measles Initiative

Because measles kills hundreds of thousands of children every year, particularly in Africa, smallpox veterans helped create the International Measles Initiative in 2001. By the end of 2008, the Measles Initiative vaccinated over 250 million children in more than 40 African countries, saving more than 3.6 million lives. By 2009, measles cases in Africa were reduced by 90%.

UNITED NATIONS FOUNDATION | **CDC** | **WHO** | **UNICEF** | **American Red Cross**

Founding members of the International Measles Initiative

In January 2007, Dr Margaret Chan, WHO Director-General, praised the achievements of the International Measles Initiative as an historic victory for public health.

Some measles immunization campaigns provide insecticidal bednets to fight malaria.

To learn more go to: *http://www.redcrossstl.org/ProgramsServices/InternationalServices/MeaslesInitiative.aspx* and: *http://www.cdc.gov/vaccines/programs/global/measlesinitiative.htm*

"Like the smallpox eradication effort, today's innovative and dedicated young public health professionals are questioning traditional boundaries perceived as limiting what can be done. They have the courage to take on apparently insoluble problems and entrenched bureaucracies; they are willingly working tirelessly ...enduring rigorous living conditions. They are working with a global vision."

Adapted from D.A. Henderson,
Lessons and Legacies of Smallpox Eradication, Smallpox — The Death of a Disease, published in 2009

Appendix I   Historic Milestones

570 CE	The word *variola* used for first time by Bishop Marius of Avenches, Switzerland.
910 CE	First medical report on smallpox, *Treatise on Smallpox and Measles*, published by Persian scholar Rhazes.
1721	Lady Mary Wortley Montague, wife of British ambassador to Turkey, learns about variolation in Turkey and introduces it to England.
1763	Allegedly the first instance of biological warfare when Lord Jeffrey Amherst approves distributing blankets from smallpox patients to Native Americans.
1796	Dr. Edward Jenner uses cowpox to vaccinate a human for the first time.
1798	Dr. Jenner publishes his findings on vaccination.
1800s	Increasingly widespread use of vaccine in Europe and U.S. reduces smallpox threat.
1923	The Russian government makes smallpox vaccination mandatory.
1950	PAHO approves smallpox eradication plan for the Americas.
1950s	Freeze-dried vaccine developed by Lister Institute in England.
1958	Soviet Epidemiologist Viktor Zhdanov proposes global eradication of smallpox to the 11th World Health Assembly (WHA).
1959	12th WHA approves a USSR resolution to eradicate smallpox.
1965	President Lyndon Johnson (USA) endorses smallpox eradication.
1966	WHA approves annual budget to support 10-year smallpox eradication and creates Smallpox Eradication Unit in Geneva with Dr. D.A. Henderson as chief.
1967	20th WHA adopts resolution for global eradication of smallpox.
1967	Ben Rubin from Wyeth Laboratories (USA) invents the bifurcated needle.
1970	Last case of smallpox occurs in West Africa.
1971	Last case of smallpox occurs in Brazil.
1972	Biological Weapons Convention agreement signed.
1975	Last case of *variola major* in the world — 3-year-old girl, Rahima Banu, from Bhola Island in Bangladesh.
1977	Last case of *variola minor* in the world — Ali Maow Maalin in Merka, Somalia.
1978	A laboratory-associated case of smallpox occurs in Birmingham, England with one death. The last non-naturally acquired case of smallpox in the world.
1980	The 33rd WHA formally declares smallpox eradicated globally.
1986	A World Health Organization (WHO) Expert Committee recommends the destruction of last remaining smallpox virus stocks in the two WHO collaborating laboratories.
1988	WHO's Smallpox Eradication Unit is closed.
1991	Smallpox virus DNA is mapped containing 186,000 pairs of DNA with 187 genes.
1996	WHA sets a deadline of 1999 for destruction of laboratory smallpox virus stocks.
1999	WHA sets a new deadline of 2002 for destruction of smallpox virus.
2002	WHA authorizes a further retention of smallpox virus stocks.
2003	The Acambis Company, with Baxter Laboratories, produces 200 million doses of new vaccine as a reserve stock.
2010	30th Anniversary of the WHA Declaration of the Eradication of Smallpox with the unveiling of Smallpox Eradication Commemorative statue on the grounds of the WHO, Geneva, Switzerland.

Appendix II - Glossary of Terms and Acronyms

Amherst	Lord Jeffrey Amherst commanding general of British forces in North America during the French and Indian war (1754-1763).
BCE	Before Current Era (formerly BC).
Bifurcated needle	A small two prong fork-like needle used to administer smallpox vaccine to the skin. Invented by Ben Rubin at Wyeth Laboratories in the 1960s.
Bouquet	Colonel Henry Bouquet, subordinate of General Amherst (1763).
Carter Center	Located in Atlanta, Georgia, and part of the Jimmy Carter Presidential Library. Dedicated to advancing human rights and alleviating unnecessary suffering.
CDC	The Centers for Disease Control and Prevention, Atlanta, Georgia, USA. An agency of the U.S. Government's Public Health Service charged with safeguarding the public health of the U.S. population.
CE	Current Era (formerly AD).
Cotton Mather	Influential Puritan preacher (1663-1728), in Boston, USA who advocated variolation to protect against smallpox.
Cowpox	A contagious disease in cows caused by a virus that is similar to *variola*, the virus that causes smallpox. In man, this disease does not cause serious illness.
DDT	Abbreviation for the chemical dichloro*diphenyltrichloroethane* which is one of the most well-known synthetic pesticides. It is a chemical with a long, unique, and controversial history.
Deworming tablets	Tablets taken orally to eliminate parasitic infections in the intestinal tract.
Diphtheria	An acute bacterial infection affecting the throat and air passages that is often fatal in young children.
DNA	*Deoxyribonucleic acid*. A nucleic acid containing basic genetic code that controls the functioning and development of living organisms.
Dracunculiasis	Commonly known as Guinea worm, a tropical infection caused by a parasite.
Eczema	A disease affecting the skin. The term *eczema* is broadly applied to a range of persistent skin conditions.
Endemic	A human infectious disease that has self-sustaining transmission in a particular geographic area.
Epidemic	An infectious disease for which the number of cases dramatically exceeds the expected levels.
Epidemiology	The study and investigation of the causes and control of diseases.
Eradication	Completely eliminating a disease so that it will not return.
Fetish	A belief attributing magic powers to an object such as a charm.
Fetisheur	A person who promotes the beliefs in magic powers.
Focus/foci	The chief site of a disease outbreak or center of an epidemic.
Freeze-dried vaccine	Vaccine that has been dried by freezing to form a powder — a better vaccine than the earlier liquid forms of smallpox vaccine.
Galen	Galen of Pergamum (129–200 CE). A prominent Roman physician and probably the most accomplished Roman medical researcher.
Guinea worm	Common term for dracunculiasis disease, a tropical parasitic infection.
Hippocrates	Ancient Greek physician considered the "father of medicine" (460-370 BCE).
Hispaniola	Caribbean island where Haiti and the Dominican Republic are located.
Humors	Ancient Greek and Roman medical belief that the human body consisted of four elements needing to be in balance for good health, personality, and complexion.
Immunization	Giving a vaccine to induce protection against a disease.
Incubation period	Time elapsed between infection and the first appearance of symptoms.
Inoculation	Another word for injecting vaccine into the body.
Insecticidal bednets	New type of bednet whose fibers incorporate a long-lasting insecticide. Mosquitoes die when they contact the bednet. These bednets are used to control malaria.
Lymph node	Oval-shaped masses of tissue in the body that act as filters for a fluid called lymph.
Measles	A highly infectious, often fatal viral disease characterized by high fever, cough, runny nose, and generalized red skin rash.
Pandemic	A disease occurring over a wide geographic area, currently defined as affecting at least two continents.
PAHO	The Pan American Health Organization, formerly Pan American Sanitary Bureau. Regional Office of the World Health Organization for the Americas.
Papule	An elevated skin lesion that does not contain fluid or pus.
Peace Corps	An agency of the U.S. government that supports volunteers for two-year international humanitarian assignments.

Appendix II - Glossary of Terms and Acronyms

Ped-O-Jet	Jet injector powered by a foot pump to inject vaccine. It was used for large scale vaccinations.
Pertussis	Also called whooping cough. a highly contagious respiratory tract infection that is sometimes fatal.
Polio	Short for poliomyelitis disease, also called infantile paralysis. A highly infectious virus that causes paralysis and sometimes death.
Pustule	A small collection of pus in the top layer of the skin or on its surface; manifestation of the first stage of smallpox disease.
Orthopoxvirus	A genus of poxviruses that includes the viruses that cause smallpox and cowpox.
Respiratory tract	Part of the human body begins with the nose and oral cavity and ends with the trachea (breathing tube).
Rhazes	Persian physician born in 910 BCE.
Ring vaccination	Vaccinating all persons around a case of smallpox, including people coming and going to and from the area of the outbreak.
Sanskrit	One of the oldest languages dating back to 1500 BCE.
SEC2010	Acronym for Smallpox Eradication Commemoration 2010.
Shapona	Smallpox god of the West African Yoruba culture.
SIDA	Swedish International Development Agency.
Sitala Mata	Hindu mother Goddess. She is thought to inflict sickness.
Smallpox	Human infectious disease caused by the variola virus.
St. Nicaise	Bishop of Rheims (France) died around 400 CE and became the patron saint of smallpox cases. His altar is still in Rheims Cathedral, France.
Surveillance and Containment	Strategy for actively finding cases and vaccinating all persons around them in order to contain the outbreak.
TaTa Industries	A major industrial and business group in India.
Tetanus	A bacterial infection also called lockjaw. An often fatal disease affecting muscles and nerves.
Thucydides	Greek historian (460-395 BCE) known as the father of scientific history.
T'ou-Shen Niang-Niang	Chinese smallpox goddess.
UN Foundation	The UN Foundation is a public charity created in 1998 with entrepreneur and philanthropist Ted Turner's support.
UNICEF	The United Nations Children's Fund.
USAID	United States Agency for International Development. The U.S. Government agency responsible for economic and humanitarian assistance worldwide.
USSR	Union of Soviet Socialist Republics which was dissolved in 1991.
Vacca	Latin word for cow from which the word vaccination is derived.
Vaccinia virus	Virus harvested from cowpox and from the skin of calves for producing smallpox vaccine.
Vaccination	Use of *vaccinia* virus to inoculate and induce smallpox immunity in humans — usually by scratching droplets of vaccine into the skin's surface.
Variola major	Latin name for the most severe type of smallpox virus. It typically killed about 30% of the people infected.
Variola minor	Latin name for the less severe type of smallpox virus that typically killed about 1% of the people infected.
Variolation	Use of smallpox scabs or pustular material from one person and inserted into the skin of another person to induce immunity.
VECTOR	State Research Center of Virology and Biotechnology located in Koltsovo, Western Siberia.
Vesicle	Small sac or bubble of liquid on the surface of the skin.
Virulent	Very strong, severe, or destructive form of infection.
Voodoo	West African word describing beliefs, spirits and practices relating to religion and deities.
WHA	The World Health Assembly, an annual gathering of member states of the World Health Organization.
WHO	The World Health Organization, with headquarters in Geneva, Switzerland and responsible for disease control and prevention coordination globally.
Yaws	A tropical infectious disease with skin eruptions.
Yellow fever	A tropical infection transmitted by the bite of a mosquito.

Appendix III
Selected List of Works Consulted

Barquet N., Domingo P. *Smallpox: the triumph over the most terrible of them ministers of death.* Ann Intern Med.1997 Oct 15;127. PMID: 9341063. Erratum in: Ann Intern Med 1998 May 1;128(9):787.

DATELINE: CDC. Centers for Disease Control, Atlanta, GA. [newsletter] Volume 11, No. 10, October 1979.

Fenner, F., D.A. Henderson, I. Arita, Z. Jesek, I.D. Ladnyi. *Smallpox and its Eradication.* Geneva: World Health Organization, 1988.

Henderson, DA. *Smallpox – The Death of a Disease*: *The Inside Story of Eradicating a Worldwide Killer.* New York: Prometheus Books, 2009.

Hopkins, DR. *Princes and Peasants: Smallpox in History*, Chicago: University of Chicago Press,1983.

Maruick C. *Smallpox virus destruction delayed yet again. JAMA.* 1995 Feb 8;273(6):446. PMID: 7837346.

Ogden, HG. *CDC and the Smallpox Crusade.* Washington, DC: US Government Printing Office, 1987. HHS Publication No. (CDC) 87-8400.

World Health Organization. *Destruction of variola virus:* [memorandum] from a WHO meeting. Bulletin World Health Organization. 1994; 72:841-4.

WORLD HEALTH: The Magazine of the World Health Organization. October 1972.

WORLD HEALTH: The Magazine of the World Health Organization. May 1980. Available from: http://whqlibdoc.who.int/smallpox/WH_5_1980.pdf.

WORLD HEALTH: The Magazine of the World Health Organization. August-September 1987: Available from:http://whqlibdoc.who.int/smallpox/WH_8-9_1987_p3.pdf.